SADLIER
VOCABULARY WORKSHOP®
ACHIEVE

Level C

Brader Jagodzinske

Jerome Shostak

Senior Series Consultant

Vicki A. Jacobs, Ed.D.
Director, Teacher Education Program
Harvard Graduate School of Education
Cambridge, Massachusetts

Series Consultants

Louis P. De Angelo, Ed.D.
Superintendent of Schools
Diocese of Wilmington
Wilmington, Delaware

John Heath, Ph.D.
Professor of Classics
Santa Clara University
Santa Clara, California

**Sarah Ressler Wright,
  M.A. English Ed, NBCT**
Head Librarian
Rutherford B. Hayes High School
Delaware, Ohio

Carolyn E. Waters, J.D., Ed.S.
Georgia Dept. of Education (Ret.)
English Language Arts Consultant
Woodstock, Georgia

Sadlier

Reviewers

The publisher wishes to thank for their comments and suggestions the following teachers and administrators, who read portions of the series prior to publication.

Cover: Concept/Art and Design: MK Advertising, Studio Montage and William H. Sadlier, Inc. Cover pencil: Shutterstock.com/VikaSuh.
Photo Credits: age fotostock/CSP_demerzel21: 40. Alamy Stock Photo/Everett Collection Inc/CSU Archives: 108; Fine Art Photographs: 100 *left*; Melanie Eldred Photography: 69 *bottom*; PRISMA ARCHIVO: 32; Gina Rodgers: 216; Everett Collection Inc: 116; GL Archive: 120; IllustratedHistory: 124 *top*; Lebrecht Music And Arts Photo Library: 192; Mary Evans Picture Library: 64; Niday Picture Library: 101 *right*; Photo Researchers, Inc / Science History Images: 196; Superstock: 101 *left*. Artville: 124 *bottom*, 125 *bottom*. Associated Press: 24 *bottom*, 213 *top right*; Nati Harnik: 69 *top*. Courtesy Central Pacific Railroad Photographic History Museum, © 2013, CPRR.org: 200 *top*. Dreamstime.com/ Sanja Baljkas: 72; Elena Duvernay: 176; Mykhailo Shcherbyna: 28; Criminalatt: 104. DRK Photo/Sid & Shirley Rucker: 169. Fotolia.com/ highwaystarz: 10. Getty Images/Roll Call: 20; Sandy Huffaker: 68; Dorothea Lange: 81; Wally McNamee: 160; George Rinhart: 13 *top right*; Bettman: 12 *bottom right*; Bettmann: 36 *bottom left*, 37 *top*, 44; Hulton Archive/Tom Munnecke: 188 *bottom*; Library of Congress/J.E. Purdy: 212; Library of Congress/Allgeier Company: 37 *bottom*; MPI/Stringer/Andrew John Russell: 200 *right*; Raleigh News & Observer/MCT/Chris Seward: 156; Science Faction/Jason Isley-Scubazoo: 112 *top*; Stringer/Johannes Simon: 189 *top*; SuperStock: 25 *top*; The LIFE Picture Collection/Margaret Bourke-White: 13 *bottom right*; TongRo Images Inc: 84. Granger, NYC: 36 *bottom right*, 125 *background*, 125 *right*, 201, 213 *top left*, 213 *top*. iStockphoto.com/fotografixx: 60. Lebrecht Music & Arts: 88. Library of Congress, Prints & Photographs Division/Prints & Photographs Division, FSA/OWI Collection, LC-USF34-016191-C/Dorothea Lange: 80 *bottom*; Prints & Photographs Division, FSA/OWI Collection, LC-USF34-016819-C/Dorothea Lange: 80 *top*. Magnum Photos/Erich Hartmann: 148. Rolf Nussbaumer: 168 *top*. Photodisc: 100 *left*, 101, 112 *background*, 113 *top right*, 125 *top*, 125, 212. PhotoEdit/Paul Conklin: 157 *top*. REUTERS/Seth Wenig: 188 *top*. REX Features Ltd/The Art Archive: 13 *top left*. Science Source/Peter Menzel: 113 *left*; Alexis Rosenfeld: 112 *bottom*; Science Photo Library/David Vaughn: 113 *right*. Shutterstock.com/Africa Studio: 101 *center*; amasterphotographer: 68 *bottom left*; Andrey Kekyalyaynen: 68 *bottom*; LANBO: 188 *left*; Peshkova: 25 *bottom*; s_oleg: 100 *right*; Sailorr: 125 *background*; shivanetua: 69 *top*; sommthink: 69 *bottom*; Subbotina Anna: 24 *top*, 25 *background*; VikaSuh: 001; Oleksii Sagitov: 100 *center*; Mihaela Stejskalova: 12 *bottom left*, 13 *top right*; blvdone: 128. Superstock/ Ambient Images Inc.: 157 *bottom*; ClassicStock.com: 152; Illustrated London News Ltd/Mar/Pantheon: 164; OLIVER TWIST PRODUCTIONS LLP/FERRANDIS, GUY/Al/Album : 204; Underwood Archives/Underwood Photo Archives : 16. The Image Works/ArenaPal/Nigel Norrington: 172; Mary Evans Picture Library: 208; Roger-Viollet: 132; Syracuse Newspapers/Chrissie Cowan: 76. U.S. National Archives: 168 *bottom*. Wikipedia: 189 *bottom*; Jeremiah Gurney: 220.

Illustration Credits: Tristan Elwell: 144, 145. Zina Saunders: 56–57.

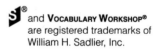 and **VOCABULARY WORKSHOP®** are registered trademarks of William H. Sadlier, Inc.

Printed in the United States of America.
ISBN: 978-1-4217-8508-0
8 9 10 11 12 BRR 24 23 22 21 20

For additional online resources, go to SadlierConnect.com.

CONTENTS

iWords Audio Program is available at **SadlierConnect.com**.

For more than five decades, VOCABULARY WORKSHOP has proven to be a highly successful tool for vocabulary growth and the development of vocabulary skills. It has also been shown to help students prepare for standardized tests. VOCABULARY WORKSHOP ACHIEVE maintains that tradition in a newly designed format.

Each of VOCABULARY WORKSHOP ACHIEVE's 15 Units introduces 20 words in two 10-word lists—**Set A** and **Set B**. Both Set A and Set B contain exercises to help you develop deeper understanding of the 10 words in each set. Combined Sets A and B then provide practice with all 20 of the words in the Unit. Review and Word Study activities follow Units 3, 6, 9, 12, and 15 and offer practice with the 60 vocabulary words in the preceding three Units.

Each level of VOCABULARY WORKSHOP ACHIEVE introduces and provides practice with 300 vocabulary words and contains features such as reading passages, writing prompts, vocabulary in context, evidence-based questions, and word study that will help you to master these new vocabulary words and succeed in using skills to comprehend unfamiliar words.

Each Unit in VOCABULARY WORKSHOP ACHIEVE consists of the following sections for **Set A** and **Set B**: an introductory **Reading Passage** that shows how vocabulary words are used in context, **Definitions** that include sentences that give examples of how to use the words, **Using Context, Choosing the Right Word**, and **Completing the Sentence**—activities that provide practice with the vocabulary words. Each introductory **Reading Passage** is a nonfiction text that includes most of the vocabulary words from the Unit to which it belongs. In addition, **Synonyms**, **Antonyms**, and **Vocabulary in Context** in combined Sets A and B round out each Unit with practice with all 20 Unit words.

The five Review sections cover all 60 words from their corresponding Units. **Vocabulary for Comprehension** is modeled on the reading sections of college entrance exams. It presents reading comprehension questions, including vocabulary-related items and evidence-based items that are based on the reading passages.

Word Study sections that contain activities on **Idioms**, **Denotation and Connotation**, and **Classical Roots** follow the Review. These sections will help you develop your understanding of figurative language and practice skills that will help you to determine the meaning of new and unfamiliar vocabulary.

The Final Mastery Test assesses a selection of words from the year and allows you to see the growth you have made in acquiring new vocabulary words and in mastering the comprehension skills you need to understand unfamiliar words.

ONLINE RESOURCES

SadlierConnect.com

Go to **SadlierConnect.com** to find iWords, an audio program that provides pronunciations, definitions, and examples of usage for all of the vocabulary words presented in this level of VOCABULARY WORKSHOP ACHIEVE. You can listen to the entire **Reading Passage** and the 20 Unit vocabulary words one word at a time, or download all of the words in any given Unit.

At **SadlierConnect.com** you will also find interactive vocabulary quizzes, flash cards, and interactive games and puzzles that will help reinforce and enrich your understanding of the vocabulary words in this level of VOCABULARY WORKSHOP ACHIEVE.

VOCABULARY IN CONTEXT

The context of a word is the printed text of which that word is part. By studying a word's context, we may find clues to its meaning. We might find a clue in the immediate or adjoining sentence or phrase in which the word appears; in the topic or subject matter of the passage; or in the physical features—such as photographs, illustrations, charts, graphs, captions, and headings—of a page itself.

The **Reading Passages** as well as the **Using Context**, **Choosing the Right Word**, **Vocabulary in Context**, and **Vocabulary for Comprehension** exercises that appear in the Units, the Reviews, and the Final Mastery Test provide practice in using context to decode and to determine the meaning of unfamiliar words.

Three types of context clues appear in the exercises in this book.

A **restatement clue** consists of a synonym for or a definition of the missing word. For example:

Faithfully reading a weekly newsmagazine not only broadens my knowledge of current events and world or national affairs but also _____ my vocabulary.

a. decreases   **b.** fragments   **c.** increases   **d.** contains

In this sentence, *broadens* is a synonym of the missing word, *increases*, and acts as a restatement clue for it.

A **contrast clue** consists of an antonym for or a phase that means the opposite of the missing word. For example:

"My view of the situation may be far too rosy," I admitted. "On the other hand, yours may be a bit (**optimistic, bleak**)."

In this sentence, *rosy* is an antonym of the missing word, *bleak*. This is confirmed by the presence of the phrase *on the other hand*, which indicates that the answer must be the opposite of *rosy*.

An **inference clue** implies but does not directly state the meaning of the missing word or words. For example:

"A treat for all ages," the review read, "this wonderful novel combines the _____ of a scholar with the skill and artistry of an expert _____."

a. ignorance . . . painter   **c.** wealth . . . surgeon

b. wisdom . . . beginner   **d.** knowledge . . . storyteller

In this sentence, there are several inference clues: (a) the word *scholar* suggests knowledge; (b) the words *novel*, *artistry*, and *skill* suggests the word *storyteller*. These words are inference clues because they suggest or imply, but do not directly state, the missing word or words.

VOCABULARY AND READING

There is a strong connection between vocabulary knowledge and reading comprehension. Although comprehension is much more than recognizing words and knowing their meanings, comprehension is nearly impossible if you do not know an adequate number of words in the text you are reading or have the vocabulary skills to figure out their meaning.

The **Reading Passages** in this level provide extra practice with vocabulary words. Vocabulary words are in boldface to draw your attention to their uses and contexts. Context clues embedded in the passages encourage you to figure out the meanings of words before you read the definitions provided on the pages directly following the passages.

Test Prep

Your knowledge of word meanings and your ability to think carefully about what you read will help you succeed in school and on standards-aligned and state exams.

The **Vocabulary for Comprehension** exercises in each Review consist of a reading passage followed by comprehension questions. The passages and questions are similar to those that you are likely to find on standards-aligned and state exams.

Types of Questions

You are likely to encounter the following types of questions in VOCABULARY WORKSHOP ACHIEVE and on standards-aligned and state exams.

Main Idea Questions generally ask what the passage as a whole is about. Often, but not always, the main idea is stated in the first paragraph of the passage. You may also be asked the main idea of a specific paragraph. Questions about the main idea may begin like this:

- The primary or main purpose of the passage is . . .

- The author's primary or main purpose in the passage is to . . .

- Which of the following statements most nearly paraphrases the author's main idea in the ninth paragraph (lines 77–88)?

- The main purpose of the fourth paragraph
  (lines 16–25) is to . . .

Detail Questions focus on important information that is explicitly stated in the passage. Often, however, the correct answer choices do not use the exact language of the passage. They are instead restatements, or paraphrases, of the text.

Vocabulary in Context Questions check your ability to use context to identify a word's meaning. For example:

- As it is used in paragraph 2, "adherents" most nearly means . . .

Use the word's context in a passage to select the best answer, particularly when the vocabulary word has more than one meaning. The answer choices may contain two (or more) correct meanings of the word in question. Choose the meaning that best fits the context.

Inference Questions ask you to make inferences or draw conclusions from the passage. These questions often begin like this:

- It can be most reasonably inferred from the information in the fifth paragraph (lines 53–69) that . . .
- The passage clearly implies that . . .

The inferences you make and the conclusions you draw must be based on the information in the passage. Using the facts you learn from the passage in addition to the knowledge and reasoning you already have helps you understand what is implied and reach conclusions that are logical.

Evidence-Based Questions ask you to provide evidence from the passage that will support the answer you provided to a previous question. These questions often begin like this:

- Which choice provides the best evidence for the answer to the previous question?
- Which statement is the best evidence for the answer to the previous question?

Questions About Tone show your understanding of the author's attitude toward the topic of the passage. To determine the tone, pay attention to the author's word choice. The author's attitude may be positive (respectful), negative (scornful), or neutral (distant). These are typical questions:

- The author's primary purpose in the passage is to . . .
- Which word best describes the author's tone?

Questions About Author's Technique focus on the way a text is organized and the language the author uses. These questions ask you to think about structure and function. For example:

- In the context of the passage, the primary function of the fourth paragraph (lines 30–37) is to . . .
- The organizational structure of the passage is best described as . . .

To answer the questions, you must demonstrate an understanding of the way the author presents information and develops ideas.

VOCABULARY AND WRITING

The **Writing: Words in Action** prompt provides you with an opportunity to practice using text evidence to respond to a prompt about the introductory **Reading Passage**. You will have the opportunity to demonstrate your understanding of the Unit words by incorporating the new vocabulary you have learned into your own writing.

WORD STUDY

Word Study helps build word knowledge with strategies to help you look closely at words for meanings. Word Study instruction and practice include **Idioms**, **Denotation and Connotation**, and **Classical Roots**.

Idioms

Three Word Study sections feature instruction on and practice with idioms. An idiom is an informal expression whose literal meaning does not help the reader or listener understand what the expression means, such as "raining cats and dogs," "the apple of my eye," or "a dark horse." While every language has its own idioms, English is particularly rich in idioms and idiomatic expressions. Developing a clear understanding of idioms will help you better understand the figurative language that authors use in their writing.

Denotation and Connotation

Instruction in **Denotation and Connotation** and practice with connotations is included in two of the Word Study sections. Understanding a word's connotation will develop your skills as a reader, writer, and speaker.

Understanding the difference between denotation and connotation is important to understanding definitions and how concepts are used, as well as in choosing the right word. In these exercises, practice choosing the correct word by determining the emotional association of the word.

Classical Roots

Each Word Study includes a **Classical Roots** exercise that provides instruction in and practice with Greek and Latin roots. Developing a useful, transferable technique to make sense out of unfamiliar words through Greek and Latin roots will help you unlock the meanings of thousands of words. An example word drawn from the vocabulary words in the previous Units is referenced at the top of the page and serves as a guide to help you complete the exercise.

PRONUNCIATION KEY

The pronunciation is indicated for every basic word in this book. The pronunciation symbols used are similar to those used in most recent standard dictionaries. The author has primarily consulted *Webster's Third New International Dictionary* and *The Random House Dictionary of the English Language* (*Unabridged*). Many English words have multiple accepted pronunciations. The author has given one pronunciation when such words occur in this book except when the pronunciation changes according to the part of speech. For example, the verb *project* is pronounced **prə jekt'**, and the noun form is pronounced **präj' ekt**.

Vowels	ā	lake	e	stress	ü	loot, *new*
	a	m*a*t	ī	kn*i*fe	ủ	foot, p*u*ll
	â	c*a*re	i	s*i*t	ə	jump, broken
	ä	b*a*rk, b*o*ttle	ō	flow	ər	b*i*rd, bet*ter*
	aủ	d*ou*bt	ô	*a*ll, c*o*rd		
	ē	b*ea*t, word*y*	oi	o*i*l		

Consonants	ch	*ch*ild, le*ct*ure	s	*c*ellar	wh	*wh*at
	g	*g*ive	sh	*sh*un	y	*y*earn
	j	*g*entle, bri*dge*	th	*th*ank	z	i*s*
	ŋ	si*ng*	th̶	*th*ose	zh	mea*s*ure

All other consonants are sounded as in the alphabet.

Stress	The accent mark follows the syllable receiving the major stress: en rich'.

Abbreviations	*adj.*	adjective	*n.*	noun	*prep.*	preposition
	adv.	adverb	*part.*	participle	*v.*	verb
	int.	interjection	*pl.*	plural		

*Read the following passage, taking note of the **boldface** words and their contexts. These words are among those you will be studying in Unit 1. It may help you to complete the exercises in this Unit if you refer to the way the words are used below.*

Greetings from the WPA
<Letters>

Twenty-five percent of workers in the United States were unemployed during the height of the Great Depression. President Franklin Delano Roosevelt's administration created the Works Progress Administration (WPA). It employed over eight million people in construction and arts projects from 1935 to 1943.

April 10, 1937
Butte, Montana

Dearest Rose,

I'd say I've been meaning to write for ages and I think of you often, but I know you loathe that sort of **servile** sentimentality, and I wouldn't want to **wrangle** about it next time we meet. Moe and I were just talking about when the three of us were together in Chicago. We got to reminiscing, and soon we were goofing around like we used to—we must have **reverted** halfway to infancy! He said you're working for the Works Progress Administration in New York. I've been writing for the WPA myself.

Things got worse in Chicago after you left. I was in and out of odd jobs, mostly out of them, and I moved back to Montana. I stayed in Missoula for a bit, at my parents' house, which is the same **citadel** of good manners and polite conversation that I remember. I'm grateful they took me in, but I felt uncomfortable about it. I don't know why I should feel like a **laggard** when everyone else is out of work, too, but it really got me down and put me in a **churlish** state of mind. After weeks of grumpily **hovering** around the house, I found work at a ranch that provided room and board.

When that job ended, I lucked into some work for the WPA. I'm writing "objective descriptions" of town, countryside, and work projects. I watched construction on the Fort Peck Dam. Now I'm in Butte, climbing through **rubble** and machinery at the copper mines nearby. By official **decree**, I'm here to record facts and figures, but I can't resist interviewing the miners, and I believe this is the best writing work I've done. I'll send you an **excerpt** once I've written more.

Send a letter if you can, or maybe I'll come see you in New York when I'm done with Butte.

Yours,
Henry

Teletype operators
in the federal office
of the WPA, 1937

FRANKLIN D. ROOSEVELT

WPA artists at work on a mural;
Woman displaying WPA poster, 1936

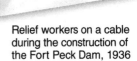

Relief workers on a cable
during the construction of
the Fort Peck Dam, 1936

June 3, 1937
New York City, New York

Dear Henry,

It's been hard times out east, too, and worse this year, just after it had seemed the country was **groping** its way back to normalcy. The only artists I know making a living with their art are working for the WPA, and I'm lucky to be one of them. I've done a series of woodcuts for posters and may soon have a chance to **collaborate** with another painter on a mural for a hospital. Some of the work that the WPA artists produce is very good, but I haven't spent as much time worrying about **plaudits** and praise as about keeping the work lined up. Around two thousand New York artists are working for the Federal Arts Project this year. The pay's not much, but I wonder what I'd be doing without it. Wonder is the beginning of wisdom, but that's a kind of wisdom I'm happy to put off.

Just back from waiting on the predictably long line for our paychecks. It's become a social event. We pass the time chatting about painting and **jostling** each other out of line for a laugh.

I can hardly imagine you in New York, but that doesn't **preclude** your arrival.

Love,
Rose

Audio

For iWords and
audio passages, go to
SadlierConnect.com.

Definitions

Note the spelling, pronunciation, part(s) of speech, and definition(s) of each of the following words. Then write the appropriate form of the word in the blank space in the illustrative sentence(s) following.

1. **bonanza**
(bə nan′ zə)

(*n.*) a rich mass of ore in a mine; something very valuable, profitable, or rewarding; a source of wealth or prosperity; a very large amount; sudden profit or gain

The movie was a box-office _____.

2. **churlish**
(chər′ lish)

(*adj.*) lacking politeness or good manners; lacking sensitivity; difficult to work with or deal with; rude

Salesclerks must avoid _____ behavior.

3. **collaborate**
(kə lab′ ə rāt)

(*v.*) to work with, work together

The students will _____ on a geology project for the annual science fair.

4. **excerpt**
(ek′ sərpt)

(*n.*) a passage taken from a book, article, etc.; (*v.*) to take such a passage; to quote

My essay has an _____ from a speech.

Place an _____ in quotation marks.

5. **grope**
(grōp)

(*v.*) to feel about hesitantly with the hands; to search blindly and uncertainly

When the power failed, we had to _____ in the dark to find a working flashlight.

6. **jostle**
(jäs′ əl)

(*v.*) to make or force one's way by pushing or elbowing; to bump, brush against; to compete for

I tried not to _____ other riders as I exited the crowded bus.

7. **laggard**
(lag′ ərd)

(*n.*) a person who moves slowly or falls behind; (*adj.*) falling behind; slow to move, act, or respond

Tour guides often have to urge _____ to keep up with the rest of the group.

Tenants who are _____ in paying rent run the risk of being forced to move.

8. **plaudits**
(plô′ ditz)

(*n., pl.*) applause; enthusiastic praise or approval

The skaters who won the gold medals gratefully accepted the _____ of their fans.

9. **revert**
(rē vərt′)

(*v.*) to return, go back

Control of a property usually _____ to the legal owner when a lease is up.

10. **vigil**
(vij′ əl)

(*n.*) a watch, especially at night; any period of watchful attention

Thousands attended the solemn _____ at the Vietnam Veterans Memorial.

Using Context

*For each item, determine whether the **boldface** word from pages 14–15 makes sense in the context of the sentence. Circle the item numbers next to the six sentences in which the words are used correctly.*

1. Over time, the abandoned mining town will crumble and **revert** to desert.

2. The bus left behind schedule because the driver had to wait for a **laggard** to arrive.

3. The audience was unsure of how to respond to the play because it was an odd **excerpt** of comedy and drama.

4. The back cover of the newly published novel was covered with **plaudits** from critics as well as famous writers.

5. When they hunt, many predators remain still for a long time and then suddenly **grope**.

6. After a chase through the park, the police officers managed to **jostle** the fleeing suspect.

7. The cold, rainy summer turned out to be a **bonanza** for the owner of the small movie theater in the beach community.

8. As we stirred the pudding over low heat on the stove, we could see it begin to **collaborate**.

9. The protest, which was entirely peaceful, ended with a candlelight **vigil** in the city's most famous square.

10. I apologized for my **churlish** behavior and promised to be more patient and courteous in the future.

Choosing the Right Word

*Select the **boldface** word that better completes each sentence. You might refer to the passage on pages 12–13 to see how most of these words are used in context. Note that the choices might be related forms of the Unit words.*

1. I chose to read a(n) (**vigil, excerpt**) from *Leaves of Grass* by Walt Whitman for my poetry recitation.

2. All those who (**jostled, collaborated**) with the enemy in the hope of gaining special favors will be punished severely.

3. She raised so many objections to attending the dance that it was obvious she was (**groping, reverting**) for an excuse not to go.

4. When I fumbled the ball on the three-yard line, the (**plaudits, excerpts**) of the crowd suddenly turned into jeers and catcalls.

5. The assembly speaker may have been boring, but that was no excuse for the students' (**laggard, churlish**) behavior toward him.

6. From the hundreds of newspaper items, the lawyer carefully (**collaborated, excerpted**) three short paragraphs that supported his case.

7. There are times when we all need to be (**jostled, reverted**) away from old, familiar ideas that may no longer be as true as they once seemed.

8. At midnight, the sentry took his post, standing (**laggard, vigil**) over the cache of weapons.

9. I refuse to accept the excuse that the pressures of a new job caused you to (**revert, grope**) to your old habit of cigarette smoking.

10. The landscape artists want to (**collaborate, revert**) with the architects so that the entire house looks as though it is part of the natural environment.

11. The principal was quick to approve new programs for our club but (**churlish, laggard**) in providing financial support for them.

12. The "broken-down old furniture" that the woman left to her children turned out to be a(n) (**bonanza, excerpt**) of valuable antiques.

Completing the Sentence

Choose the word from the word bank that best completes each of the following sentences. Write the correct word or form of the word in the space provided.

bonanza	collaborate	grope	laggard	revert
churlish	excerpt	jostle	plaudits	vigil

1. If you will only show a little patience, that business investment may grow into a(n) __bonanza__ for you.

2. For two nights, he did his homework faithfully; then he __reverted__ to his usual lazy ways.

3. The swiftest members of the herd escaped the trappers' nets, but the __laggard__ were caught.

4. Let me read aloud a few __excerpts__ from the newspaper review of the new movie.

5. You hurt her feelings when you reacted to her comments in such a(n) __churlish__ way, especially since you asked for her advice.

6. A single word of praise from the coach meant more to me than all the loud but thoughtless __plaudits__ of the crowd.

7. When the lights suddenly went out, I __virgil__ my way into the kitchen to find a candle and matches.

8. The cafeteria line was so crowded that I was __jostle__ past the desserts before I could take one.

9. Our teacher gave the two of us permission to __collaborate__ on our reports because we were investigating related problems.

10. With tireless devotion, the ailing child's parents kept an anxious __grope__ at her bedside.

Definitions

Note the spelling, pronunciation, part(s) of speech, and definition(s) of each of the following words. Then write the appropriate form of the word in the blank space in the illustrative sentence(s) following.

1. adage
(ad′ ij)

(*n.*) a proverb, wise saying
One way to begin an informal speech or an oral report is to quote an old _____.

2. citadel
(sit′ ə del)

(*n.*) a fortress that overlooks and protects a city; any strong or commanding place
A medieval _____ once guarded the capital city of the Greek island of Rhodes.

3. decree
(di krē′)

(*n.*) an order having the force of law; (*v.*) to issue such an order; to command firmly or forcefully
Caesar Augustus issued a _____ that all the world be taxed.
Why does nature always seem to _____ nasty weather for our annual family picnic?

4. discordant
(dis kôr′ dənt)

(*adj.*) disagreeable in sound, jarring; lacking in harmony
Their little spat struck a _____ note in our otherwise happy family get-together.

5. evolve
(ē välv′)

(*v.*) to develop gradually; to rise to a higher level
Authors hope that their notes, descriptions, and character sketches will _____ into a book.

6. hover
(həv′ ər)

(*v.*) to float or hang suspended over; to move back and forth uncertainly over or around
A large group of vultures _____ in the air above the wounded animal.

7. preclude
(prē klüd′)

(*v.*) to make impossible, prevent, shut out
Three wrong answers will _____ any contestant from entering the quiz show's final round.

8. rubble
(rəb′ əl)

(*n.*) broken stone or bricks; ruins
Bulldozers and wrecking balls soon reduced the damaged building to a heap of smoking
_____.

9. servile
(sər′ vīl)

(*adj.*) of or relating to a slave; behaving like or suitable for a slave or a servant, menial; lacking spirit or independence, abjectly submissive

Most serious performers prefer constructive criticism to _____ flattery.

10. wrangle
(raŋ′ gəl)

(*v.*) to quarrel or argue in a noisy, angry way; to obtain by argument; to herd; (*n.*) a noisy quarrel

My brother and sister always _____ over whose turn it is to take out the trash.

The customer got into a nasty _____ with the shopkeeper.

Using Context

*For each item, determine whether the **boldface** word from pages 18–19 makes sense in the context of the sentence. Circle the item numbers next to the six sentences in which the words are used correctly.*

1. No matter how intelligent you are, no one will want to work with you if you keep up that **servile** attitude and continue bossing others around.

2. The temperature continued to **hover** above freezing for a week before it plummeted.

3. When the principal entered the noisy auditorium, he wasted no time in issuing a **decree** that everyone be quiet.

4. While using an **adage** or two can be effective when making a point, you need to include some original thoughts as well.

5. I wonder how two people with such **discordant** personalities can remain friends.

6. Volunteers helped clean up the **rubble** after the hurricane struck the seaside town.

7. The teacher felt the students' enthusiasm **evolve** as she handed out the pop quiz.

8. That broken-down old cottage is as good as a **citadel**.

9. I'm not sure why the customer continues to shop here, since she always proceeds to **wrangle** with the salespeople over the cost and quality of the products.

10. When I saw how stressed and distracted my mother was, I was able to **preclude** that now was not the best time to ask for a raise in my allowance.

Choosing the Right Word

*Select the **boldface** word that better completes each sentence. You might refer to the passage on pages 12–13 to see how most of these words are used in context. Note that the choices might be related forms of the Unit words.*

1. Under the Articles of Confederation, the thirteen states (**hovered, wrangled**) so much that the nation seemed to be in danger of breaking up.

2. After I had broken curfew for the third time in one week, my angry parents (**precluded, decreed**) that I was grounded for the rest of the term.

3. A president needs advisors who will frankly explain what they really think, rather than just offer (**servile, discordant**) agreement and constant approval.

4. For weeks, an anxious world (**wrangled, hovered**) between war and peace as diplomats desperately struggled to resolve the crisis.

5. I have always regarded our colleges and universities as (**citadels, decrees**) of learning and bastions against ignorance and superstition.

6. The committee found it impossible to reach any agreement on the matter because the views of its members were so (**servile, discordant**).

7. The little club that they set up to talk over community problems (**evolved, precluded**) over the years into a national political organization.

8. I hate when people (**hover, wrangle**) over me when I'm on my computer.

9. As we searched through the (**rubble, citadel**) after the earthquake, it was heartbreaking to find such articles as a teakettle and a child's doll.

10. Every time he quotes an old (**rubble, adage**), he looks as though he has just had a brilliant new idea.

11. The fact that he was found guilty of a felony many years ago doesn't (**evolve, preclude**) his running for mayor.

12. After much (**wrangling, precluding**), the student council was able to convince the principal to give students more passing time between classes.

Completing the Sentence

Choose the word from the word bank that best completes each of the following sentences. Write the correct word or form of the word in the space provided.

adage	decree	evolve	preclude	servile
citadel	discordant	hover	rubble	wrangle

1. Suddenly the ___discordant___ voices of two quarreling people burst upon my ears and jarred me out of my daydream.

2. During his eleven years of "personal rule," King Charles I of England bypassed Parliament and governed the country by royal ___decree___.

3. As we discussed our coming vacation, we gradually ___evolve___ a plan for a bicycle trip through New England.

4. They had such a long ___wrangle___ over the use of the bicycle that their mother finally forbade either of them from using it.

5. What is the exact wording of the ___adage___ about early birds and worm-catching?

6. The Emancipation Proclamation of 1863 was the first step in releasing African Americans from their ___servile___ bonds.

7. On the ground, teams of paramedics administered first aid to the victims of the accident, while police helicopters ___hover___ overhead.

8. After the walls of their city fell to the enemy, the inhabitants withdrew to the ___citadel___ and continued the struggle from there.

9. Before the new housing project could be built, it was necessary to tear down the old houses and remove the ___rubble___.

10. Your silly pride about doing everything on your own ___preclude___ your getting the help you need so badly.

Synonyms

*Choose the word or form of the word from this Unit that is the same or most nearly the same in meaning as the **boldface** word or expression in the phrase. Write that word on the line. Use a dictionary if necessary.*

1. kept a **lookout** while the soldiers slept _____

2. tried to **prohibit** further objections to the bill _____

3. **scrabble** for an answer to the question _____

4. crushed beneath many tons of **debris** _____

5. tried to attack the **fort** at midnight _____

6. **proclaimed** that there would be no more homework _____

7. annoyed by all that **fawning** attention _____

8. used an **extract** from the book for her report _____

9. became a **slowpoke** after her foot injury _____

10. an inspiring **motto** to live by _____

11. **returned** to old habits _____

12. received **acclaim** for an outstanding performance _____

13. **lingered** on the subject of his past mistakes _____

14. represented quite a **bonus** for the company _____

15. **shoved** the table so hard that it tipped over _____

Antonyms

*Choose the word or form of the word from this Unit that is most nearly opposite in meaning to the **boldface** word or expression in the phrase. Write that word on the line. Use a dictionary if necessary.*

1. surprised by the **melodious** ending of the piece _____

2. a theory that **shrivels** when put into practice _____

3. exhibit **courteous** behavior _____

4. decided to **work alone** on the project _____

5. refused to **concur** with his opponent on the issue _____

Writing: Words in Action

Do you think that teens should be expected to pitch in by getting jobs or doing chores or volunteer work? Write a brief essay in which you support your opinion with specific examples from your personal experience, reading (pages 12–13), and prior knowledge. Use three or more words from this Unit.

Vocabulary in Context

*Some of the words you have studied in this Unit appear in **boldface** type. Read the passage below, and then circle the letter of the correct answer for each word as it is used in context.*

For Americans keeping a worried **vigil** over the economy in 1933, recovery from the Great Depression was far from certain. After the stock market crash of 1929, unemployment soared to 25 percent. The desperate conditions in the United States were part of a worldwide economic crisis. The U.S. election of 1932 marked a turning point, with fresh leadership committed to a drastic rescue of economy.

In a popular **adage,** President Franklin D. Roosevelt told the country "we have nothing to fear but fear itself." His economic relief programs of the New Deal were known as "alphabet soup." The federal government established literally dozens of new agencies; each one of them was known by an abbreviation of its full name. Most of these agencies were not the product of presidential **decree** through an executive order, but instead were authorized and created by Congress. The force behind the majority of them, however, was Roosevelt.

None of these agencies became more famous than the Tennessee Valley Authority (TVA), created in 1933 to control floods, facilitate navigation, improve living standards, and produce electrical power in the Tennessee River region. This agency embarked on a massive program of building dams and flood-control projects, as well as hydroelectric generating stations. The TVA offered citizens of seven states a **bonanza** of benefits.

More than 80 years later, the TVA mission continues to **evolve.** The agency now focuses on clean nuclear energy and on environmental stewardship. Privately owned power companies have sounded some **discordant** notes regarding the TVA's production and sale of electrical power. However, the TVA is still widely respected.

---

1. What is the meaning of **vigil** as it is used in paragraph 1?

a. forecast   **c.** survey
b. watch   **d.** summary

2. What is the meaning of **adage** as it is used in paragraph 2?

a. proverb   **c.** acronym
b. paraphrase   **d.** jingle

3. Decree comes from the Latin word **decretum. Decretum** most likely means

a. surgery   **c.** subsidy
b. reform   **d.** decision

4. The word **bonanza** means about the same as

a. stash   **c.** windfall
b. payback   **d.** drought

5. Which word means the same as **evolve** as it is used in paragraph 4?

a. flare up   **c.** deflate
b. unfold   **d.** resound

6. What does **discordant** most likely mean as it is used in paragraph 4?

a. agreeable   **c.** grating
b. unanimous   **d.** partial

*Read the following passage, taking note of the **boldface** words and their contexts. These words are among those you will be studying in Unit 2. It may help you to complete the exercises in this Unit if you refer to the way the words are used below.*

Instant Cash!
<Expository Essay>

Who can imagine life today without an Automated Teller Machine (ATM)? They are available in **bountiful** numbers throughout the world. Yet that virtually indispensable dispenser of cash is less than half a century old!

The first mechanical cash dispenser was the brainchild of an **enterprising** Turkish-American inventor, Luther George Simjian. His 200 patents included devices such as flight simulators, a meat tenderizer, and self-posing portrait cameras. When the idea of an automated banking machine struck him, he registered 20 patents before any bank agreed to give it a trial run. It is easy to assume that the inventor of such a popular machine was laughing all the way to the bank. Simjian's cash

Luther George Simjian

machine, however, did not prove **durable**. Within six months of its installation in New York City in 1939, the device was removed due to lack of customer acceptance.

It was not until 1967, nearly thirty years later, that Barclays Bank, in a **gingerly** launch, cautiously rolled out a self-service machine in London, England, that proved successful. The mechanism was relatively primitive, at least by today's standards. The first cash machines relied on customers' use of prepaid tokens to retrieve envelopes with a fixed amount of cash inside.

Soon afterward, many other banks became **avowed** champions of the cash machine. The banks' ostensible rationale was customer service. But it would be foolish to **minimize** the many advantages that cash machines proffered to the banks themselves. By the late 1970s, the highest fixed cost for the average large bank was its branches. The greatest variable cost and **detriment** to profits were its staff. Cash deposits and cash withdrawals accounted for a veritable **glut** of a typical bank's transactions. With their perennially **frugal** eye, bank accountants swiftly recognized that self-service operations could reduce branch staff costs by 70 percent.

Experts quickly determined that public acceptance of ATMs pivoted on convenience, simplicity, speed, security, and trust. Location, in particular, was a key factor. For maximum efficiency, ATMs had to be located near public transport or in a shopping mall, not at a branch. The busier and more **congested** the location, apparently, the better. Now, roughly 75 percent of all cash dispensed by banks to their customers comes from cash machines. Devices that were originally spurned by the public are now **venerated** as essential institutions. Public acceptance of deposits by machine was significantly slower than customers' usage of ATMs for withdrawals. In general, it seems that customers still prefer and trust an over-the-counter transaction for deposits.

The future of the ATM seems assured. However, cash machines pose some interesting, unanswered questions. Will banks succeed, for example, in persuading their customers to **veer** away from long-ingrained habits and to utilize ATMs as often for deposits as for withdrawals? Will banks develop **oblique** advertising pitches, ingeniously slotted into the ATM program and calculated to exploit revenue opportunities?

And what about security? An intriguing option is the issue of biometrics for customer

Bank customers wait in line for a teller.

identification. Everyone today knows about the problem of passwords. There are simply too many of them in people's lives. So the possibility that customers will be able to identify themselves at the neighborhood ATM by, say, using a fingerprint on the screen or through face recognition (biometrics) might herald a real improvement. Biometrics will most likely **invalidate** the cunning plans of **wanton** impostors. Now firmly established, ATMs may have an interesting future ahead of them.

For iWords and audio passages, go to SadlierConnect.com.

Technology scan of a man's hand

Definitions

Note the spelling, pronunciation, part(s) of speech, and definition(s) of each of the following words. Then write the appropriate form of the word in the blank space in the illustrative sentence(s) following.

1. avowed
(ə vaúd')

(*adj., part.*) declared openly and without shame, acknowledged

The governor was an _____ supporter of the plan to aid public libraries throughout the state.

2. bountiful
(baúnt' i fəl)

(*adj.*) giving freely, generous; plentiful, given abundantly

On Thanksgiving Day people all over America celebrate the _____ gifts of nature.

3. congested
(kən jest' id)

(*adj., part.*) overcrowded, filled or occupied to excess

The doctor grew very concerned when the patient's lungs became _____ with fluid.

4. enterprising
(ent' ər prī ziŋ)

(*adj.*) energetic, willing and able to start something new; showing boldness and imagination

An _____ young person may turn a hobby into a way of earning money.

5. gingerly
(jin' jər lē)

(*adj., adv.*) with extreme care or caution

Difficult and demanding customers should be handled in a _____ and courteous manner.

People walked _____ along the streets.

6. glut
(glət)

(*v.*) to provide more than is needed or wanted; to feed or fill to the point of overstuffing; (*n.*) an oversupply

Hollywood studios _____ theaters with big-budget action movies during the summer season.

When there is a _____ of gasoline on the market, prices at the pump may drop dramatically.

7. incognito
(in käg nē' tō)

(*adj., adv.*) in a disguised state, under an assumed name or identity; (*n.*) the state of being disguised; a person in disguise

Just before the battle of Agincourt, Shakespeare's King Henry V prowls through his camp _____.

In a way makeup artists are practitioners of the fine art of _____.

8. minimize
(min' ə mīz)

(v.) to make as small as possible, make the least of; to make smaller than before

Whenever you are in a car, you should wear your seatbelt to _____ the risk of injury in an accident.

9. veer
(vēr)

(v.) to change direction or course suddenly, turn aside, shift

The huge storm finally _____ out to sea.

10. wanton
(wänt' ən)

(adj.) reckless; heartless, unjustifiable; loose in morals; (n.) a spoiled, pampered person; one with low morals

The brave superhero soon put a stop to the evil villain's acts of _____ cruelty.

The main character in the popular miniseries was a charming but heartless _____.

Using Context

*For each item, determine whether the **boldface** word from pages 26–27 makes sense in the context of the sentence. Circle the item numbers next to the six sentences in which the words are used correctly.*

1. The food critic visits restaurants and orders meals **incognito** to ensure that he will not receive special treatment because of his position.

2. Knowing they were about to embark on a **bountiful** journey, the crew was withdrawn.

3. Let's plan to leave at 10:00 because the subway will be less **congested** then.

4. It is impossible to scold the puppy when he looks at you with those sweet, **gingerly** eyes.

5. The truck driver had to **veer** to the left to avoid hitting the deer that had suddenly appeared.

6. After the floodwaters receded, it became clear that the bridge that crossed the river was in **wanton** need of repair.

7. Volcanic eruptions occur in places where there is a **glut** in Earth's rocky crust.

8. The 95-year-old yoga teacher was an **avowed** believer in the benefits of daily exercise.

9. People who are highly allergic to dust must take measures to **minimize** their exposure to it.

10. The **enterprising** young woman started her own pet-sitting business when she was just 16 years old.

Choosing the Right Word

*Select the **boldface** word that better completes each sentence. You might refer to the passage on pages 24–25 to see how most of these words are used in context. Note that the choices might be related forms of the Unit words.*

1. Building a new skyscraper there will bring thousands of additional people into an area that is already (**incognito, congested**).

2. We were shocked by their (**bountiful, wanton**) misuse of the money their parents had left them.

3. Although I love sports, I sometimes feel that television is becoming (**minimized, glutted**) with athletic events of all kinds.

4. Instead of just waiting for things to get better by themselves, we must be more (**avowed, enterprising**) in working for improvements.

5. I will not try to (**minimize, veer**) the difficulties we face, but I am sure that we can overcome them by working together.

6. April wrapped her puppy's wound (**gingerly, incognito**) to avoid causing the pup any more pain.

7. Instead of approaching him timidly and (**bountifully, gingerly**), tell him frankly what is on your mind.

8. We are grateful for the (**congested, bountiful**) legacy that our great artists and composers have given us.

9. The politician tried to (**glut, minimize**) his role in the cover-up.

10. Your speech would have been better if you had stayed with your main idea instead of (**veering, glutting**) off to side issues.

11. Why do you suppose someone whose face is known all over the world would want to travel (**gingerly, incognito**)?

12. As a(n) (**avowed, gingerly**) supporter of women's rights, she believes that men and women should receive the same pay if they do the same jobs.

Completing the Sentence

Choose the word from the word bank that best completes each of the following sentences. Write the correct word or form of the word in the space provided.

avowed	congested	gingerly	incognito	veer
bountiful	enterprising	glut	minimize	wanton

1. We admired the _enterprising_ immigrant who set up a small shop and developed it into a large and prosperous business.

2. The film star traveled _incognito_ in order to avoid the attention of her adoring fans.

3. While I do not wish to alarm you, I will not _minimize_ the danger if you refuse to have the entire herd vaccinated.

4. What a change from the _congested_ streets of the inner city to the wide-open spaces of the Great Plains!

5. We should be willing to share our _bountiful_ food supplies with less fortunate people in other parts of the world.

6. We desperately needed every bit of help we could find, but what we got was a(n) _glut_ of advice and a scarcity of cold cash.

7. To avoid the children in the street, the truck _veered_ sharply to the right and sideswiped several parked cars.

8. The vandals broke windows, overturned desks, and left the school a scene of _____ destruction.

9. Isn't it strange for a(n) _avowed_ music lover to show no interest in our school orchestra?

10. I was afraid of banging my bare feet against the furniture, so I walked through the darkened room very _gingerly_.

Definitions

Note the spelling, pronunciation, part(s) of speech, and definition(s) of each of the following words. Then write the appropriate form of the word in the blank space in the illustrative sentence(s) following.

1. antics
(an' tiks)

(*n. pl.*) ridiculous and unpredictable behavior or actions

The _____ of the chimpanzees amused the crowds at the zoo.

2. banter
(ban' tər)

(*v.*) to exchange playful remarks, tease; (*n.*) talk that is playful and teasing

There is nothing my friends and I enjoy more than to _____ good-naturedly for hours.

Casual _____ helps to pass the time during a long journey.

3. detriment
(det' rə mənt)

(*n.*) harm or loss; injury, damage; a disadvantage; a cause of harm, injury, loss, or damage

The home team survived a six-game losing streak with almost no _____ to its standing in the league.

4. durable
(dúr' ə bəl)

(*adj.*) sturdy, not easily worn out or destroyed; lasting for a long time; (*n. pl.*) consumer goods used repeatedly over a series of years

Denim is a very _____ kind of fabric.

Many people own household _____ such as furniture and appliances.

5. frugal
(frü' gəl)

(*adj.*) economical, avoiding waste and luxury; scanty, poor, meager

At home, we usually prepare _____ but nourishing and delicious meals.

6. invalidate
(in val' ə dāt)

(*v.*) to make valueless, take away all force or effect

Lawyers will try to _____ the contract.

7. legendary
(lej' ən der ē)

(*adj.*) described in well-known stories; existing in old stories (legends) rather than in real life

Ajax was one of the _____ Greek heroes who fought before the walls of Troy.

8. maim
(mām)

(*v.*) to cripple, disable, injure, mar, disfigure, mutilate

Each year, accidental falls _____ thousands of people, some of them for life.

9. **oblique**
(ō blēk′)

(*adj.*) slanting or sloping; not straightforward or direct
The boxer's _____ blow left his
opponent unscathed.

10. **venerate**
(ven′ ə rāt)

(*v.*) to regard with reverence, look up to with great respect
In a number of cultures, it is customary for people to
_____ the oldest members of society.

Using Context

*For each item, determine whether the **boldface** word from pages 30–31 makes sense in the context of the sentence. Circle the item numbers next to the six sentences in which the words are used correctly.*

1. I had to interrupt the friends' **banter** several times to get them to focus on the serious subject at hand.

2. His **oblique** manner of speaking may seem abrupt to some, but I appreciate it when someone gets straight to the point.

3. The neighbor's **frugal** tone of voice indicated that he did not see my baseball hitting his car as a laughing matter.

4. My friend proceeded to **venerate** our math teacher after receiving a low grade on the test, unaware that she was within earshot.

5. When it came to light that the student body president had arranged the prank, everyone was shocked that our supposed role model would engage in such **antics**.

6. Because she was attacked by a dog as a young girl, she feared that any animal she came across would **maim** her.

7. I am on a mission to find some **durable** shoes that will withstand the large amount of walking I do on a daily basis.

8. I prepared for the debate by thinking of ways to **invalidate** any point my opponent might make.

9. The football field was reduced to such **detriment** after the rainstorm that it was hardly recognizable.

10. Only in my dreams do I have the strength of the **legendary** hero Hercules and can lift a car right over my head.

Choosing the Right Word

*Select the **boldface** word that better completes each sentence. You might refer to the passage on pages 24–25 to see how most of these words are used in context. Note that the choices might be related forms of the Unit words.*

1. The mad Roman emperor Caligula believed that he was a god and expected people to (**venerate, invalidate**) him.

2. Imagine our surprise when we found a trunk full of albums recorded by the (**legendary, frugal**) performer Ray Charles.

3. Detectives turn off the lights and use soft beams at the scene of a crime, as evidence is easier to see in (**durable, oblique**) lighting.

4. Orders for (**legendary, durable**) goods such as computers and cell phones were up this year, thanks to a recent boost in our economy.

5. Because of his repeated traffic violations, his driver's license has been (**venerated, invalidated**).

6. It was bad taste on your part to use that (**venerating, bantering**) tone when we were discussing such a sad event.

7. Our friendship has proved to be (**oblique, durable**) because it is based on mutual respect and honesty.

8. When they saw that they had been caught red-handed, they resorted to all kinds of (**detriments, antics**) in a vain attempt to prove their "innocence."

9. Children may be (**maimed, venerated**) in spirit as well as in body if they do not have a secure and loving home environment.

10. After living for so long on a (**frugal, durable**) diet, I was amazed when I saw the variety of rich dishes served at the banquet.

11. Self-confidence is a good quality; but if it is carried too far, it can be a (**detriment, banter**) to success in life.

12. I didn't want Charlotte to know that I was watching her, but occasionally I managed to steal a few (**oblique, legendary**) glances at her.

Completing the Sentence

Choose the word from the word bank that best completes each of the following sentences. Write the correct word or form of the word in the space provided.

antics	detriment	frugal	legendary	oblique
banter	durable	invalidate	maim	venerate

1. In American law, the fact that the person accused of a crime is poor does not _____invailidate_____ his or her right to adequate legal representation.

2. Although he had been severely _____maimed_____ in the automobile accident, he was determined to return to his job and lead a normal life.

3. As Americans, we _____venerate_____ the great ideals of human freedom expressed in the Bill of Rights.

4. Davy Crockett was a real person, but so many tall tales have been told about him that he has become a(n) _____ledgendary_____ figure.

5. Although she tried to cover it up with lively _____bantar_____, I could see that her feelings had been deeply hurt.

6. An inability to get along smoothly and effectively with other people will be a great _____detriment_____ to you in any career you may choose.

7. I would never have expected members of the senior class to take part in such childish _____antics_____!

8. His income was small, but his _____frugal_____ living habits enabled him to save a large sum of money over the years.

9. Instead of walking straight from the farmhouse to the road, we set off in a(n) _____oblique_____ direction across the field.

10. Even the most _____durable_____ materials will in time be damaged by flowing water.

Synonyms

*Choose the word or form of the word from this Unit that is the same or most nearly the same in meaning as the **boldface** word or expression in the phrase. Write that word on the line. Use a dictionary if necessary.*

1. cared for those **wounded** in the fire   _____
2. **joked** with my teammates after the game   _____
3. annoyed by an **excess** of junk mail   _____
4. made **ambitious** plans for the company   _____
5. walked **cautiously** on the ice   _____
6. saved his money and lived a **thrifty** lifestyle   _____
7. an **abundant** harvest of pumpkins   _____
8. asked the question in an **indirect** way   _____
9. facts that **discredit** the theories   _____
10. surprised by the **unprovoked** attack   _____
11. a **confirmed** opponent of higher taxes   _____
12. used **strong** rope to tie the boxes together   _____
13. **underrated** the importance of the discovery   _____
14. **swerved** to avoid a pothole   _____
15. laughed at the **tomfoolery** of the comedian   _____

Antonyms

*Choose the word or form of the word from this Unit that is most nearly opposite in meaning to the **boldface** word or expression in the phrase. Write that word on the line. Use a dictionary if necessary.*

1. a witness who testifies **openly**   _____
2. a diary written by an **unknown** source   _____
3. streets that are **unimpeded by** cars and pedestrians   _____
4. the **advantage** of a small car   _____
5. **despised** by his neighbors   _____

Writing: Words in Action

Suppose you work for an advertising agency. A bank has asked you to create a commercial promoting the use of its ATM. Your ad copy should include at least two details from the passage (pages 24–25), prior knowledge, and observations. Use three or more words from this Unit.

Vocabulary in Context

*Some of the words you have studied in this Unit appear in **boldface** type. Read the passage below, and then circle the letter of the correct answer for each word as it is used in context.*

We all know the scene where the mastermind enters the password that opens the safe, unlocks the computer, or saves the world. We have seen it in innumerable movies. The **antics** are pretty much the same in every case, and so is the **banter** between the characters.

"But how could you possibly have known the password for his account?"

"I didn't. But it's no secret that he believes he was the **legendary** figure Cuchulain in another life. So I just typed in Cuchulain and, sure enough, that is his password."

In any password-protected system, the weak link is always the password. A password reveals a lot about a person—and a person reveals a lot about a password. To make a password unique and memorable, we tend to use information significant only to ourselves. We use birthdays, birthplaces, personal interests, pets' names, and family stuff. We also tend to use the same password more than once.

These days, we are warned to be **frugal** with personal information. Making your personal information known to others makes it difficult to remain **incognito** in the digital world. A weak password can **maim** a system's security. We are advised to use "strong" passwords that include capital letters, numerals, and special characters. We are cautioned not to store them, but to remember them. The problem is that most of us have upwards of 20 passwords to remember, and the stronger we make them, the harder they are to remember.

In case you forget, most vendors of password-sensitive products provide a simple solution. As you are setting up your product, you are offered a number of questions to which only you know the answers, such as pets' names, birthday, and birthplace.

---

1. What is the meaning of **antics** as it is used in paragraph 1?
   a. capers
   b. plotting
   c. actions
   d. intentions

2. The word **banter** means about the same as
   a. debate
   b. angry words
   c. playful chat
   d. comedy

3. In paragraph 3, what does the word **legendary** suggest about Cuchulain?
   a. He is a soldier.
   b. He is a historical figure.
   c. He is a great leader.
   d. He exists only in legend.

4. **Frugal** comes from the Latin word **frugalis. Frugalis** most likely means
   a. thoughtful
   b. thrifty
   c. knowing
   d. slavish

5. Which word means the same as **incognito** as it is used in paragraph 5?
   a. disguised
   b. insincere
   c. famous
   d. private

6. What does **maim** most likely mean as it is used in paragraph 5?
   a. bypass
   b. unsettle
   c. disable
   d. disengage

*Read the following passage, taking note of the **boldface** words and their contexts. These words are among those you will be studying in Unit 3. It may help you to complete the exercises in this Unit if you refer to the way the words are used below.*

Grand Columbian Carnival Unites the World

<Press Release>

FOR IMMEDIATE RELEASE

World's Columbian Exposition to Open

Chicago Rolls Out Red Carpet for World Visitors

Chicago, Illinois— Drum roll, please! After years of **prodigious** preparation and immense hard work, the World's Columbian Exposition, celebrating the 400th anniversary of Christopher Columbus's landing in America, opens to the public on May 1, 1893. It's spectacular! It's **audacious**! It's like nothing you've ever seen before!

Come one, come all, and experience the great World's Fair on the shores of Lake Michigan. President Grover Cleveland will be on hand to officially cut the ribbon.

Hundreds of thousands of electric lightbulbs will light up the night sky and illuminate the buildings. There will be exhibits from each state in the union and from many foreign countries that show the **relevant** inventions, achievements, and wares of each. Commercial, agricultural, scientific, and artistic industries will be represented. Flags of the world will be **tethered** together in harmony.

It promises to be the greatest monument to human progress witnessed thus far.

But the Fair will offer much more than homage to hard work and ingenuity. The organizers have **amassed** a plethora of captivating sideshows and entertainment. The Midway Plaisance has been **allotted** as the site for musical reviews and street buskers, dancing, and carnival rides— including Mr. George Ferris's magnificent Chicago Wheel, standing 250 feet tall and offering a bird's-eye view of the Fair.

There is sailing on the lake and lagoons, and gondola rides on the Venetian waterways and canals. A long, moving sidewalk along the lakefront pier will take you to the casino—for just a nickel a ticket! Norway is sending a life-sized model of a Viking ship, and the Liberty Bell is traveling from Philadelphia aboard a flatbed rail car. Pyrotechnics and fireworks will herald the arrival of a replica of Columbus's vessels from Spain. Plus, the Hall of Agriculture will feature an 11-ton "Monster Cheese" sent by Canada and a 1500-pound chocolate Venus de Milo (no sampling allowed!).

Postcard depicting an aerial view of the World's Columbian Exposition

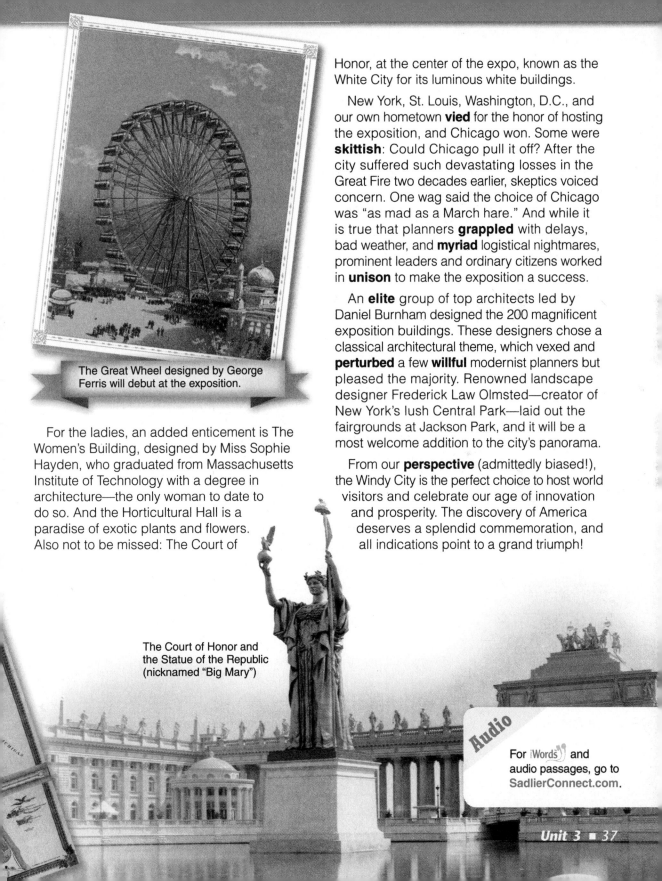

The Great Wheel designed by George Ferris will debut at the exposition.

Honor, at the center of the expo, known as the White City for its luminous white buildings.

New York, St. Louis, Washington, D.C., and our own hometown **vied** for the honor of hosting the exposition, and Chicago won. Some were **skittish**: Could Chicago pull it off? After the city suffered such devastating losses in the Great Fire two decades earlier, skeptics voiced concern. One wag said the choice of Chicago was "as mad as a March hare." And while it is true that planners **grappled** with delays, bad weather, and **myriad** logistical nightmares, prominent leaders and ordinary citizens worked in **unison** to make the exposition a success.

An **elite** group of top architects led by Daniel Burnham designed the 200 magnificent exposition buildings. These designers chose a classical architectural theme, which vexed and **perturbed** a few **willful** modernist planners but pleased the majority. Renowned landscape designer Frederick Law Olmsted—creator of New York's lush Central Park—laid out the fairgrounds at Jackson Park, and it will be a most welcome addition to the city's panorama.

From our **perspective** (admittedly biased!), the Windy City is the perfect choice to host world visitors and celebrate our age of innovation and prosperity. The discovery of America deserves a splendid commemoration, and all indications point to a grand triumph!

For the ladies, an added enticement is The Women's Building, designed by Miss Sophie Hayden, who graduated from Massachusetts Institute of Technology with a degree in architecture—the only woman to date to do so. And the Horticultural Hall is a paradise of exotic plants and flowers. Also not to be missed: The Court of

The Court of Honor and the Statue of the Republic (nicknamed "Big Mary")

Audio

For iWords and audio passages, go to SadlierConnect.com.

Definitions

Note the spelling, pronunciation, part(s) of speech, and definition(s) of each of the following words. Then write the appropriate form of the word in the blank space in the illustrative sentence(s) following.

1. allot
(ə lät′)

(*v.*) to assign or distribute in shares or portions
The teacher _____ books and supplies to each student on the first day of school.

2. audacious
(ô dā′ shəs)

(*adj.*) bold, adventurous, recklessly daring
The audience cheered the _____ feats of the trapeze artists.

3. comply
(kəm plī′)

(*v.*) to yield to a request or command
Employees who fail to _____ with a company's rules may lose their jobs.

4. grapple
(grap′ əl)

(*n.*) an iron hook used to grab and hold; (*v.*) to come to grips with, wrestle or fight with
A ship equipped with _____ may be used to recover large pieces of wreckage from the ocean floor.
Store employees _____ with the thieves and held them until the police arrived.

5. instigate
(in′ stə gāt)

(*v.*) to urge on; to stir up, start, incite
Several demonstrators in the angry crowd did their best to _____ a riot.

6. myriad
(mir′ ē əd)

(*adj.*) in very great numbers; (*n.*) a very great number
Scientists continue to make new discoveries in their studies of the _____ life-forms of the jungle.
You will find information about a _____ of subjects on the Internet.

7. prodigious
(prə dij′ əs)

(*adj.*) immense; extraordinary in bulk, size, or degree
Few intellects have rivaled the _____ mind of Albert Einstein.

8. skittish
(skit′ ish)

(*adj.*) extremely nervous and easily frightened; shy or timid; extremely cautious; unstable, undependable
Only an experienced and confident rider should mount a _____ horse.

9. tether
(teth′ er)

(n.) a rope or chain used to fasten something to a fixed object; the outer limit of strength or resources; (v.) to fasten with a rope or chain

Some young people find it difficult to break the emotional and financial _____ that bind them to their parents.

Before the storm, I _____ the boat securely to the dock.

10. unison
(yü′ nə sən)

(n.) a sounding together; agreement or accord

The members of our new student orchestra need to practice playing in _____.

Using Context

*For each item, determine whether the **boldface** word from pages 38–39 makes sense in the context of the sentence. Circle the item numbers next to the six sentences in which the words are used correctly.*

1. When I asked, "Who wants to go to the playground?" all answered in **unison**, "I do!"

2. Health inspectors often visit restaurants to see if they **comply** with the city's health codes.

3. The school budget will **allot** money to necessities such as teacher salaries, transportation, and building maintenance.

4. Scientists will use the latest computer models to **instigate** the path of the tremendous storm.

5. I would urge you to be careful and make an **audacious** rather than impulsive choice.

6. The main character of the humorous story has to continually **grapple** with the challenges of being a new kid at school.

7. So far, no one has been able to solve the **myriad** of what happened to the missing results of the scientific study.

8. After a car accident, it's understandable to feel **skittish** about getting into a car again.

9. Wouldn't it be nice to **tether** away a long summer afternoon on a beautiful beach with no deadlines or responsibilities to worry about?

10. The moon landing was a **prodigious** accomplishment that can be attributed to the dedication and hard work of a great many people.

Choosing the Right Word

*Select the **boldface** word that better completes each sentence. You might refer to the passage on pages 36–37 to see how most of these words are used in context. Note that the choices might be related forms of the Unit words.*

1. As I glanced upward at the giant sequoia, I realized how (**prodigiously, audaciously**) tall these trees truly are.

2. By the twentieth mile of a marathon, many runners have reached the end of their (**unison, tether**).

3. As I stared at the luscious chocolate swirl cake, I bravely (**instigated, grappled**) with temptation—but the chocolate cake won!

4. Mr. Ponce knew that it was Tyler who blew the whistle in class, as Tyler is always (**tethering, instigating**) trouble.

5. Great new discoveries in science can be made only by men and women with intellectual (**compliance, audacity**).

6. In the next chorus, *please* try to sing in (**unison, compliance**).

7. I wonder why the camp directors were unwilling to (**comply, grapple**) with my request to keep a pet snake in my tent.

8. My neighbor has all kinds of colorful kites and wind socks (**instigated, tethered**) to stakes in her yard, claiming that they keep the deer from eating her plants.

9. Can you imagine what a (**skittish, prodigious**) amount of research is needed for a multivolume reference book such as the *Encyclopaedia Britannica*?

10. He has had such bad experiences with motorcycles that he has become extremely (**audacious, skittish**) of them.

11. Our course in life sciences has given us some idea of the (**myriad, unison**) varieties of plants and animals inhabiting the earth.

12. If we have to share the same locker, please try to keep your things in the space (**allotted, complied**) to you.

Completing the Sentence

Choose the word from the word bank that best completes each of the following sentences. Write the correct word or form of the word in the space provided.

allot	comply	instigate	prodigious	tether
audacious	grapple	myriad	skittish	unison

1. Before we set out on the camping trip, our Scout leader _**alloted**_ special tasks and responsibilities to each one of us.

2. There in the middle of the garden was a goat _**tethered**_ to a stake.

3. The autumn night sky, with its _**myriad**_ stars, always fills me with awe and wonder.

4. When he seemed hopelessly defeated, General George Washington crossed the Delaware River and launched a(n) _**audacious**_ surprise attack on the Hessians.

5. You will have to use a(n) _**grapple**_ to recover the lobster trap from the bottom of the bay.

6. Though we have made many outstanding contributions to the conquest of space, landing men on the moon is probably our most _**prodigious**_ achievement.

7. Trying to navigate through rush-hour traffic on a high-speed expressway can be a nightmare for a(n) _**skittish**_ driver.

8. If all the members of the cast work in _**unison**_, I am sure we will have a successful class show.

9. I refuse to _**comply**_ with any order issued by a person who has absolutely no knowledge of the project I'm working on.

10. In wartime, it is not unusual for secret agents to be sent behind enemy lines in an effort to _**instigate**_ a rebellion.

Definitions

Note the spelling, pronunciation, part(s) of speech, and definition(s) of each of the following words. Then write the appropriate form of the word in the blank space in the illustrative sentence(s) following.

---

1. amass
(ə mas′)

(*v.*) to bring together, collect, gather, especially for oneself; to come together, assemble

A prudent investor can _____ a fortune in the stock market over the long run.

---

2. devoid
(di void′)

(*adj.*) not having or using, lacking

The old well on my grandparents' property has long been _____ of water.

---

3. elite
(ā lēt′)

(*n.*) the choice part of a group of people or things; (*adj.*) superior

Each year, the social _____ of the community sponsors several events to benefit local charities.

You can get a fine education regardless of whether you attend an _____ school.

---

4. incapacitate
(in kə pas′ ə tāt)

(*v.*) to deprive of strength or ability; to make legally ineligible

In the 1940s and 1950s, polio _____ many thousands of people each year all over the world.

---

5. longevity
(län jev′ ə tē)

(*n.*) long life, long duration, length of life

The sea turtle is known for its _____.

---

6. perspective
(pər spek′ tiv)

(*n.*) a point of view or general standpoint from which different things are viewed, physically or mentally; the appearance to the eye of various objects at a given time, place, or distance

The designs for the children's playhouse were drawn to scale and in the right _____.

---

7. perturb
(pər tərb′)

(*v.*) to trouble, make uneasy; to disturb greatly; to throw into confusion

The rude and disruptive behavior of several party guests _____ the host and hostess.

---

8. relevant
(rel′ ə vənt)

(*adj.*) connected with or related to the matter at hand

I found several Web sites that provided information _____ to the topic of my research paper.

---

9. vie
(vī)

(*v.*) to compete; to strive for victory or superiority
Many actors _____ for the leading role in the famous director's new film.

10. willful
(wil′ fəl)

(*adj.*) stubbornly self-willed; done on purpose, deliberate
After lengthy deliberations, the jury found the defendant guilty of _____ murder.

Using Context

*For each item, determine whether the **boldface** word from pages 42–43 makes sense in the context of the sentence. Circle the item numbers next to the six sentences in which the words are used correctly.*

1. While this conversation is interesting, it is not **relevant** to our original discussion, so I will table it for another time.

2. It was just my luck that the flu happened to **incapacitate** me right before my job interview, forcing me to reschedule for the following week.

3. Reading books allows me not only to learn about different parts of the globe, but also to see the world from the **perspective** of people from other backgrounds.

4. After a hard day, nothing can **vie** my spirits more than some relaxing time spent with good friends.

5. The sight of the sky **devoid** of clouds forced everyone to leave the park in preparation for the coming downpour.

6. The speaker's voice was full of such **longevity** that even those who had expressed no interest in the subject were moved by his passion.

7. Nothing can **perturb** the toddler more than the sight of blowing bubbles, which he will delightedly run after and try to catch.

8. The student continued to break the rules after receiving several warnings, so she was suspended due to her **willful** disobedience.

9. She has been working two jobs every summer for the past few years in order to **amass** the money she will need to pay for college tuition.

10. The wealthy man insisted that only the most **elite** group of surgeons be allowed to operate on his wife.

Choosing the Right Word

Select the **boldface** word that better completes each sentence. You might refer to the passage on pages 36–37 to see how most of these words are used in context. Note that the choices might be related forms of the Unit words.

1. Jane Addams was not only profoundly (**perturbed, amassed**) by the suffering of other people but also tried hard to help them.

2. She had devoted her life to (**amassing, incapacitating**) not material riches but the love, respect, and thanks of every member of this community.

3. (**Willful, Perturbed**) with her son's lazy ways, Ms. Lowry called the boy into the house, demanding that he clean up his room immediately.

4. The bitter strike closed shops, shut down factories, and (**incapacitated, vied**) an entire industry for months.

5. People who come from rich and socially prominent families don't always belong to the intellectual (**perspective, elite**).

6. How do you explain the fact that in practically every country the (**elite, longevity**) of women is greater than that of men?

7. I don't think anyone can hope to (**vie, perturb**) with Gloria in the election for "Most Popular Student."

8. Do you really think your story is (**relevant, willful**) to this conversation?

9. Perhaps in the long-term (**longevity, perspective**) of history, some events that seem very important now will prove to be minor.

10. We will never have a well-organized or effective club if all the members insist (**willfully, perturbedly**) on having their own way.

11. She delivered a simple, low-key speech, completely (**devoid, relevant**) of fancy language or emotional appeals.

12. The defense has told you about the defendant's unhappy childhood, but how is this (**relevant, willful**) to the question of innocence or guilt?

Completing the Sentence

Choose the word from the word bank that best completes each of the following sentences. Write the correct word or form of the word in the space provided.

amass	elite	longevity	perturb	vie
devoid	incapacitate	perspective	relevant	willful

1. We can thank modern medical science for the increased _____ of human beings in most parts of the world.

2. I know that you are a brilliant student, but I am still amazed that you could _____ such a vast store of information so quickly.

3. Someday, when you see this event in its proper _____, you will realize that it is not as important as it seems now.

4. Dad said, "I am _____ not because you failed the exam, but because you seem unable to understand *why* you failed it."

5. I am completely _____ of sympathy for anyone who loses a job because of carelessness and indifference.

6. The _____ child insisted on wearing sneakers to her sister's wedding.

7. Since the town meeting tonight has been called to deal with conservation, only discussion _____ to that subject will be allowed.

8. A number of cities _____ with one another to be chosen as the site of a national political convention.

9. The disease had so _____ the poor woman that she was no longer able to leave her bed.

10. He joined the _____ group of athletes who have run a mile in under four minutes.

Synonyms

*Choose the word or form of the word from this Unit that is the same or most nearly the same in meaning as the **boldface** word or expression in the phrase. Write that word on the line. Use a dictionary if necessary.*

1. **doled out** four tickets to each member of the cast _____

2. chose only the **select few** _____

3. **struggled** with the lock on the door _____

4. **innumerable** ways to say hello _____

5. felt **jumpy** around large spiders _____

6. **contend** with a rival team for the championship _____

7. told to stick to the **pertinent** details _____

8. **deliberate** act of protest _____

9. **tie up** the dog to the fence _____

10. could only see things from her **viewpoint** _____

11. had **tremendous** knowledge on the subject _____

12. had **daring** plans to take over the company _____

13. arrived at **consensus** on the course of action _____

14. **accumulated** a huge collection of folk art _____

15. repeated delays that **irritated** the passengers _____

Antonyms

*Choose the word or form of the word from this Unit that is most nearly opposite in meaning to the **boldface** word or expression in the phrase. Write that word on the line. Use a dictionary if necessary.*

1. left the army **restored** _____

2. arrested for **disobeying** the law _____

3. the **brevity** of the public's interest in the story _____

4. called in to **suppress** the protestors _____

5. a river **teeming with** fish _____

Writing: Words in Action

Suppose that you are one of the sponsors for the World Exposition. You want to persuade visitors to attend this event. Write a brochure enticing visitors, using examples from your reading (pages 36–37), personal experiences, and prior knowledge. Use three or more words from this Unit.

Vocabulary in Context

*Some of the words you have studied in this Unit appear in **boldface** type. Read the passage below, and then circle the letter of the correct answer for each word as it is used in context.*

World's fairs come and go, but some of the stunning architectural feats created for these international exhibitions have had **longevity** over the years. Some paragons of architecture that still stand today were originally constructed for world's fairs. The Eiffel Tower in Paris and the Palace of Fine Arts in San Francisco were originally built to **comply** with architects' idealized visions of the future.

The Eiffel Tower was built for the 1889 World's Fair by engineer Gustave Eiffel and architect Stephen Sauvestre. Some Parisians decided to **amass** significant opposition to this 1063-foot-tall creation near the Champ de Mars; many of these opponents were angry enough to **instigate** protests and riots. This challenge did not **incapacitate** Eiffel and Sauvestre—they continued to build the Eiffel Tower. Though many believed that the Eiffel Tower would only last 20 years, the Eiffel Tower is currently the world's most visited monument by ticket sales, and it has contributed $435 billion euros to the French economy.

The Palace of Fine Arts in San Francisco was built for the Panama-Pacific Exposition: the 1915 World's Fair that celebrated the completion of the Panama Canal. This building was an important step in rebuilding San Francisco 10 years after an earthquake and a fire left the city **devoid** of many buildings. Bernard Maybeck initially designed the structure to be temporary; it was supposed to be demolished after the fair ended. In 1964, the City of San Francisco rebuilt the structure out of concrete, and it remains a popular sightseeing venue.

---

1. In paragraph 1, what does the word **longevity** suggest about the architecture?
  a. It was important.
  b. It was long-lived.
  c. It was made poorly.
  d. It was unique.

2. What is the meaning of **comply** as it is used in paragraph 1?
  a. connect with
  b. compare to
  c. contrast with
  d. yield to

3. Amass comes from the Latin word **massa**. **Massa** most likely means
  a. mask
  b. match
  c. mass
  d. master

4. Which word means the same as **instigate** as it is used in paragraph 2?
  a. incite
  b. stop
  c. propose
  d. perceive

5. The word **incapacitate** means about the same as
  a. silence
  b. satisfy
  c. facilitate
  d. debilitate

6. What does **devoid** most likely mean as it is used in paragraph 3?
  a. lacking
  b. full
  c. glowing
  d. restricted

Vocabulary for Comprehension
Part 1

*Read "How News Travels," which contains words in **boldface** that appear in Units 1–3. Then answer the questions.*

How News Travels

During the eighteenth century, news traveled at the speed of a sailing ship, or of a galloping horse. Until the mid-nineteenth century journeys overland

(5) could be as slow and torturous as ocean voyages. In 1776 it took as long for news of the U.S. Declaration of Independence to reach London by sea from Philadelphia as it did to reach El Paso by land. Delays

(10) were legendary. When Benjamin Franklin served as U.S. Ambassador in Paris from 1776 through 1785, he often waited up to six months for replies to his dispatches.

The art of diplomacy thrived during

(15) the long pauses caused by slow communication. Ambassadors were especially **relevant** to international relations at that period in history. Nations would constantly **vie** for dominance, especially in

(20) Europe, and ambassadors often had to act on their own initiative because there was not enough time to wait for governmental go-ahead. Their powers were enormous. An ambassador's decision could change

(25) the course of history. In addition, the delays caused by long-distance travel allowed time for tempers to cool. Delays gave ambassadors the opportunity to practice thoughtful, diligent diplomacy. They

(30) provided political leaders a chance to work toward long-term solutions to complex problems, rather than short-term fixes.

Electric telegraphy converts written messages into electric impulses. These

(35) impulses travel long distances instantly by wire to remote receivers, where they are converted back into readable text. Various forms of electric telegraph were developed

in the early nineteenth century, but none

(40) of them succeeded in sending messages more than a few miles. During the 1830s and 1840s, electrical scientists in several countries competed to develop a workable long-distance electric telegraph system.

(45) By the mid-nineteenth century, electric telegraphy had **evolved** into its historically familiar form. Not everyone welcomed the new technology—the international diplomatic community has always been

(50) **laggard** to incorporate new technologies. When he received his first telegram, British Foreign Secretary Lord Palmerston roared, "By God, this is the end of diplomacy!" Nevertheless, London, like every other

(55) European foreign ministry, adopted it during the early 1850s. And the electric telegraph did not invalidate the role of the diplomat. The rapidity of transmission put political leaders and diplomats under new

(60) pressures. International disputes now intensified at a speed that posed new challenges to foreign ministries, which had relied for so long on delay as a tool in resolving international discord. Telegraphy

(65) did not play a part in the diplomacy of the United States until the completion of the first reliable transatlantic cable in1866.

Diplomacy by telegraph lasted until the late twentieth century, when it was

(70) replaced by computer technology and fiber optic cables—which carry light rather than electricity. Whatever form diplomatic communications take in he future, the **avowed** intention will

(75) always remain the same: to help nations **collaborate** and to avoid conflict.

1. Which word means the opposite of **relevant**?
   A) pertinent
   B) courteous
   C) obstinate
   D) unsuitable

2. What does the word **vie** most likely mean as it is used in line 19?
   A) war
   B) compete
   C) press
   D) wait

3. What is the main purpose of the second paragraph?
   A) to stress the crucial function of diplomacy in international relations
   B) to describe the work of ambassadors with the electric telegraph.
   C) to criticize eighteenth century diplomacy
   D) to show how diplomacy ignores time

4. As it is used in line 46, what does the word **evolved** mean?
   A) diminished
   B) corroded
   C) developed
   D) united

5. **Part A**
   Why did Lord Palmerston regard the electric telegraph as the end of diplomacy?
   A) He did not trust the new technology.
   B) He did not trust diplomats who used the new technology.
   C) The message was addressed to him.
   D) Its rapidity allowed no time for the exercise of diplomacy.

   Part B
   Which choice provides the **best** evidence for the answer to the previous question?
   A) "Franklin served as U.S. Ambassador in Paris" (lines 10–11)
   B) "diplomacy thrived during the long pauses" (lines 14–15)
   C) "Ambassadors were especially relevant" (lines 16–17)
   D) "Nations would constantly vie for dominance" (lines 18–19)

6. According to the passage, why did the United States start to use the electric telegraph later than European nations?
   A) European nations were close to each other.
   B) Progress was delayed by the Civil War.
   C) The United States was reluctant to adopt the new technology.
   D) There was no reliable transatlantic cable until 1866.

7. What is the meaning of **laggard** as it is used in line 50?
   A) unwilling
   B) swift
   C) sluggish
   D) reluctant

8. What does the word **avowed** most likely mean as it is used in line 74?
   A) understood
   B) declared
   C) unstated
   D) anticipated

9. Which word is closest in meaning to the word **collaborate** as it is used in line 76?
   A) connive
   B) struggle
   C) work hard
   D) work together

10. What is the main idea of the passage?
    A) Diplomacy does not always rely on the most efficient available means of communication.
    B) The electric telegraph has always been the most efficient form of international communications.
    C) It is always the intention of international diplomacy to avoid war by all available means.
    D) International diplomacy is directly affected by developments in communication technology.

Vocabulary for Comprehension
Part 2

*Read this passage, which contains words in **boldface** that appear in Units 1–3. Then choose the best answer to each question based on what is stated or implied in the passage. You may refer to the passage as often as necessary.*

Questions 1–10 are based on the following passage.

On June 11, 1776, Congress appointed a committee to prepare a formal declaration of independence from Great Britain. The committee consisted of John Adams,
(5) Benjamin Franklin, Thomas Jefferson, Robert R. Livingston, and Roger Sherman. At 33 years of age, Jefferson was the youngest member of the committee. He had only become a member of
(10) Congress a year before, and both Adams and Franklin had experience, rank, and reputation that far exceeded his. But when the committee voted on who would write the first draft, they **allotted** the task
(15) to Jefferson. Adams came second.

Forty-six years later, in August 1822, Timothy Pickering wrote to John Adams to ask why the committee had chosen Jefferson to write the Declaration. Why
(20) didn't Jefferson's age and inexperience **preclude** him from such a responsibility? By the time Adams received this request for information he was 87 years old. He had served as Washington's vice-
(25) president from 1789 to 1797, and as president from 1797 to 1801. Jefferson had been Adams's vice-president, but they had become political rivals. Adams was a Federalist, and Jefferson was a
(30) Democratic-Republican. Jefferson had beaten Adams to the presidency in the election of 1800. When Adams replied to Pickering, however, he was not **churlish.** His reply is illuminated by his great
(35) generosity of spirit. He says nothing to Jefferson's **detriment** and clearly **venerates** Jefferson. He is **bountiful** in his admiration and affection for his great rival.

Adams explains that when Jefferson
(40) entered Congress in 1775, he brought with him a reputation for expertise in literature and science. According to Adams, Jefferson's fellow congressmen quickly noted that his writing had a
(45) "peculiar felicity of expression" (this phrase, like other quoted passages, is **excerpted** from Adams's letter). He had earned many **plaudits** on congressional committees for being "prompt, frank,
(50) explicit and decisive." It was for these qualities, Adams wrote, that Jefferson "seized upon my heart." Jefferson won his vote, and Adams did his best to secure the votes of his colleagues in favor of
(55) Jefferson. Adams had courage and integrity, but his writing lacked Jefferson's grace. Franklin was an expert in many fields of thought—and a genius in some—but his writing lacked Jefferson's
(60) concentration and power of persuasion.

When Jefferson won the vote he proposed that Adams should write the first draft. Adams refused. He told Jefferson that because the Commonwealth of
(65) Virginia was the oldest and most eminent of the colonies, tradition demanded that the Declaration should come from a Virginian. He told Jefferson that he—Jefferson—had none of the revolutionary
(70) baggage that burdened him, Franklin, and the others: "I am obnoxious, suspected, and unpopular." Jefferson denied Adams's claims, and still refused to **comply** with his wishes, Adams said simply, "You
(75) can write ten times better than I can." According to Adams, that settled it.

"Well," said Jefferson, "if you are decided, I will do as well as I can."

1. As it is used in line 14, "allotted" most nearly means
  A) assigned.
  B) delivered.
  C) conveyed.
  D) consigned.

2. As it is used in line 21, "preclude" most nearly means
  A) qualify.
  B) deter.
  C) disqualify.
  D) condemn.

3. As it is used in line 33, "churlish" most nearly means
  A) forgetful.
  B) rude.
  C) grateful.
  D) vengeful.

4. The author's intention in the second paragraph (lines 16–38) is to
  A) introduce Pickering, who provokes Adams to explain the mystery of why Jefferson was chosen.
  B) explain how, over the years, mutual admiration might have soured into rivalry and bitter enmity.
  C) focus on Adams, and to show how the careers of Jefferson and Adams drew them together and pushed them apart.
  D) show how Jefferson and Adams were politically and temperamentally opposites.

5. Which of the following is the best paraphrase for "a peculiar felicity of expression" (line 45)?
  A) an unusually attractive way of speaking
  B) a uniquely compelling way with language
  C) an unlikely turn of phrase
  D) a rare figure of speech

6. It can reasonably be inferred from the passage that Thomas Jefferson
  A) was in competition with Adams in 1776.
  B) thought little of Adams's writing abilities.
  C) became more friendly with John Adams as the years passed.
  D) had great respect and affection for John Adams in 1776.

7. Which choice provides the best evidence for the answer to the previous question?
  A) Lines 37–38 ("He ... great rival")
  B) Lines 50–52 ("It was ... heart")
  C) Lines 61–63 ("When ... first draft")
  D) Lines 77–78 ("'Well ... I can")

8. Adams refused to write the first draft
  A) because Jefferson had won the vote, so the task was his.
  B) because he thought Jefferson's offer was meant politely, but not seriously.
  C) because he believed Jefferson was in every way the best man for the job.
  D) because he was disappointed at having lost the vote to Jefferson.

9. As it is used in line 73, the word "comply" most nearly means
  A) understand.
  B) consent.
  C) reject.
  D) display.

10. Which of the following best summarizes the passage?
  A) Adams explains why his rival and friend Jefferson came to write the first draft of the Declaration of Independence.
  B) John Adams receives a letter that forces him to cast his mind back 46 years and face some uncomfortable truths.
  C) Adams considers his anger about the choice of Jefferson to write the first draft over him and Benjamin Franklin.
  D) After a lifetime in politics, Adams finally accepts the reasons why Jefferson was picked to draft the Declaration of Independence.

Synonyms

*From the word bank below, choose the word that has the same or nearly the same meaning as the **boldface** word in each sentence and write it on the line. You will not use all of the words.*

avowed	incapacitate	laggard	skittish
detriment	incognito	oblique	unison
grope	instigate	perturb	veer
hover	invalidate	revert	venerate

1. Having natural talent can be more of a **hindrance** than an advantage, because people sometimes expect more from you. _____

2. Many younger brothers tend to **worship** their older brothers throughout their childhoods. _____

3. It is hard to understand why a **sworn** sports fanatic would rather watch games on television than attend them live. _____

4. Some parents say that the teacher is **sluggish** in responding to their emails, but she is just ensuring her replies are accurate. _____

5. The scenes in the film we so gory as to **upset** some of the moviegoers enough that a few of them left before the end. _____

6. I was grateful that the credit card company was able to **cancel** the purchases that were made with my account after someone stole my wallet. _____

7. My younger brother tends to **regress** to childlike behavior when he wants something from our parents. _____

8. The residents of the seaside town feared that the news of polluted water in their bay would **cripple** their tourism industry. _____

9. The girl is a little **jumpy** around dogs because of an upsetting experience when she was a child. _____

10. As I watched my friend **linger** by the doorway, I knew he was mustering the courage to ask our teacher about his poor grade. _____

11. I don't know how we'll ever get a group of such different people to actually work in **harmony**. _____

12. The **indirect** route to the airport was inconvenient, but we were able to avoid the heavy traffic on the highway. _____

Two-Word Completions

Select the pair of words that best completes the meaning of each of the following sentences.

1. It isn't wise to give very young children toys that will break easily. They need playthings that are _____ because they haven't yet learned to handle fragile items _____.
   a. frugal ... willfully
   b. prodigious ... wantonly
   c. servile ... churlishly
   d. durable ... gingerly

2. If you are careless with your money, you will always be penniless. But if you are _____, you may be able to _____ a sizable personal fortune.
   a. frugal ... amass
   b. audacious ... preclude
   c. bountiful ... evolve
   d. enterprising ... maim

3. "If he weren't so rude, I'd be glad to _____ with him on the project," I said. "But I don't think I can work with someone with such a _____ manner."
   a. vie ... congested
   b. banter ... relevant
   c. collaborate ... churlish
   d. wrangle ... servile

4. The clownish _____ of cartoon characters, both animal and human, have won the hearts and _____ of many generations of delighted children.
   a. antics ... plaudits
   b. banter ... bonanzas
   c. tethers ... decrees
   d. adages ... vigils

5. The TV marathon not only garnered _____ amounts of money for the region's starving millions but also yielded an unexpectedly rich _____ of publicity for their plight.
   a. legendary ... allotment
   b. prodigious ... bonanza
   c. bountiful ... banter
   d. myriad ... rubble

6. He was a man of great energy and _____. In no time at all, he rose from relatively humble beginnings to the very _____ of power.
   a. longevity ... antics
   b. audacity ... durables
   c. compliance ... perspectives
   d. enterprise ... citadels

7. "A person has to expect a little accidental bumping and pushing in a crowded bus," I observed to my companion. "It's just not possible to avoid _____ another passenger when the center aisle is _____ with people."
   a. grappling ... elite
   b. maiming ... devoid
   c. jostling ... congested
   d. minimizing ... glutted

Idioms

In the passage about the World's Columbian Exposition (see pages 36–37), the writer states that at least one person viewed the choice of Chicago as the host city as "mad as a March hare."

"Mad as a March hare" is an idiom that means "showing little reason" or "foolish." An **idiom** is a figure of speech; the words are not to be interpreted literally. Idioms are informal expressions that are unique to every language. Although idioms are colorful and expressive, they should be used sparingly in formal writing.

Choosing the Right Idiom

*Read each sentence. Use context clues to figure out the meaning of each idiom in **boldface** print. Then write the letter of the definition for the idiom in the sentence.*

1. Ms. Robins is **one smart cookie**, so she's not going to believe that the dog ate your homework. _____

2. Zander better expect to **pony up** if he wants to buy that fancy motorcycle. _____

3. My best friend, Brianna, and I are always **on the same wavelength**. _____

4. Although Jack was in agonizing pain, he **kept a stiff upper lip** until the paramedics arrived. _____

5. The tutor was **banging his head against the wall** trying to explain algebra to me. _____

6. Unfortunately, the plans for the new pedestrian bridge have been **put on ice**. _____

7. The boss thinks Eddie is a **bad egg**, and she wants me to watch him closely. _____

8. There were so many sales that I was able to buy this dress **for a song**. _____

9. My little nephews **fight like cats and dogs**, so I don't enjoy babysitting them. _____

10. I've gone over the house **with a fine tooth comb**, and I can't find my ring anywhere. _____

a. pay or contribute some money

b. postponed

c. someone who is not easy to deceive

d. acted bravely or showed no fear

e. bicker; argue intensely

f. in great detail; thoroughly

g. someone who can't be trusted

h. in agreement

i. at a low price; for very little

j. frustrated after several unsuccessful attempts

Classical Roots

vers, vert—to turn

This Latin root appears in **revert** (page 15), which means "to return, to go back to a previous, or lower, condition." Some other words based on the same root are listed below.

controversy	inverse	reversal	verse
conversant	pervert	traverse	vertiginous

From the list of words above, choose the one that corresponds to each of the brief definitions below. Write the word in the blank space in the illustrative sentence below the definition. Use a dictionary if necessary.

1. to travel across; to cross and recross; to extend over

We plan to _____ the countryside by bicycle this summer.

2. turned upside down or inside out; referring to a relationship in which one item increases as the other decreases

Division is the _____ of multiplication.

3. a line of poetry; poetic writing (*"a turning, as of a line"*)

The teacher asked each student to recite a _____ of a favorite poem.

4. whirling or spinning; tending to make dizzy; affected by or suffering from dizziness

The _____ rides in amusement parks are popular with children of all ages.

5. to turn away from the right course; to lead astray, distort (*"thoroughly, utterly turned"*)

The defendant was accused of paying bribes to try to _____ the justice system.

6. a change or overthrow; a change of fortune (*usually for the worse*), setback

The press criticized the Supreme Court's _____ of the state court's decision.

7. familiar by use or study; acquainted (*"turning with"*)

Before we remodeled our house, we sought expert advice from someone _____ with the town's building code.

8. a lengthy dispute (*"a turning against"*)

A new development in medical technology may spark a heated _____ within the field.

*Read the following passage, taking note of the **boldface** words and their contexts. These words are among those you will be studying in Unit 4. It may help you to complete the exercises in this Unit if you refer to the way the words are used below.*

Toni Cade Bambara
<Author Profile>

Toni Cade Bambara (1939–1995) wore many hats during her lifetime: writer, editor, teacher, filmmaker, activist, and social worker. Born in Harlem, she came of age during the civil rights movement and the stirrings of feminism. Bambara **deplored** social injustice. Her disapproval spurred her to work hard to **oust** injustice from American society. Her career united diverse interests in a single-minded effort to build and **bolster** equality and tolerance.

As a young woman, Bambara lived in New York City. She gained a faculty position at Livingston College, a new unit of Rutgers University designed to serve underprivileged students. She achieved academic recognition by editing the landmark anthology *The Black Woman* (1970). This collection featured poems, essays, and stories by stellar African American writers, including Alice Walker, Audre Lorde, and Nikki Giovanni. When one **peruses** the anthology today, it is hard to imagine that no one before Bambara had attempted such a project.

Two years later, Bambara **mustered** a group of short stories for her publication entitled *Gorilla,*

My Love. It decisively **annulled** any doubt that Bambara was a major new voice in American fiction. The stylistic traits that her work was **prone** to are clearly visible: urban settings, first-person narrators, the theme of community, and an uncanny mastery of the spoken word. For Bambara, urban language was far from **frivolous**. Instead, she used it to plunge the reader into a real and edgy world. Bristling with sassy humor, Bambara's leading characters are often young black girls who refuse to knuckle under to prejudice or disrespect. Strong and self-reliant, they feel no **qualms** about talking back, as is shown by Squeaky, the narrator in one of Bambara's best-known stories, "Raymond's Run." Squeaky may not have been born on Easy Street, but as portrayed by Bambara, she possesses a wealth of wisdom and compassion at an early age.

During the 1970s and 1980s, Bambara **sustained** a hectic schedule of teaching, writing, and social and political activism. Her first novel, *The Salt Eaters* (1980), focuses on a fictional community organizer, Velma Henry. After suffering a nervous breakdown, Velma seeks **recourse** with an untraditional healer. In the novel, Bambara presents illness and pain as metaphors for social and political oppression. Health issues **obsess** many of the characters. The novel presents multiple perspectives and an intricate, experimental structure. *The Salt Eaters* won the American Book Award and the Langston Hughes Society Award in 1981.

During this period, Bambara was also active in documentary film work. Such films, she felt, could shake up indifferent viewers who had become **blasé** or **staid** about injustice and inequality. Her script for the film *The Bombing of Osage Avenue* (1986) received best documentary awards from the Pennsylvania Association of Broadcasters and the National Black Programming Consortium.

It was also during this period that Bambara began the novel that many critics consider her masterpiece: *Those Bones Are Not My Child*. Harrowing and suspenseful, the novel presents a city caught in the grip of political and racial tensions. Sadly, Bambara did not live to complete this work. She died of cancer on December 9, 1995. The Nobel Prize-winning novelist Toni Morrison, ever **solicitous** of her good friend Bambara, saw the book through to publication. Bambara's work remains popular and is often included in anthologies of notable stories for young adults.

Audio

For iWords and audio passages, go to SadlierConnect.com.

Definitions

Note the spelling, pronunciation, part(s) of speech, and definition(s) of each of the following words. Then write the appropriate form of the word in the blank space in the illustrative sentence(s) following.

1. bolster
(bōl′ stər)

(*v.*) to support, give a boost to; (*n.*) a long pillow or cushion; a supporting post

When you write a research paper, you should always use appropriate facts to _____ your case.

The sofa has four comfortable _____.

2. deplore
(di plôr′)

(*v.*) to feel or express regret or disapproval

Social critics _____ what they believe is a widespread decline in good manners.

3. frivolous
(friv′ ə ləs)

(*adj.*) of little importance, not worthy of serious attention; not meant seriously

I'll ignore your _____ suggestion.

4. obsess
(äb ses′)

(*v.*) to trouble, haunt, or fill the mind

If you allow fear of failure to _____ you, you will find it difficult or even impossible to achieve your goals in life.

5. oust
(aůst)

(*v.*) to remove, drive out of a position or place

Military leaders _____ the duly elected president and took over the government.

6. porous
(pôr′ əs)

(*adj.*) full of tiny holes; able to be penetrated by air or water

Some synthetic materials are as _____ and strong as natural sponges.

7. prone
(prōn)

(*adj.*) lying facedown; inclined, likely

Unfortunately, I am _____ to earaches and sinus infections.

8. qualm
(kwäm)

(*n.*) a pang of conscience, uneasiness, misgiving, or doubt; a feeling of faintness or nausea

Don't you have serious _____ about voting for such a relatively unknown and inexperienced candidate?

9. **residue**
(rez′ ə dü)

(*n.*) a remainder, that which remains when a part has been used up or removed

A _____ of sticky taffy made the pan difficult to clean.

10. **staid**
(stād)

(*adj.*) serious and dignified; quiet or subdued in character or conduct

Many companies have a dress code which requires that all employees wear _____ colors such as navy or gray.

Using Context

*For each item, determine whether the **boldface** word from pages 58–59 makes sense in the context of the sentence. Circle the item numbers next to the six sentences in which the words are used correctly.*

1. Some jobs, such as that of a security guard or ambulance dispatcher, require people to have a calm and **staid** manner.

2. In order to receive a perfect score in this game, a player must answer each history or geography question without a single **qualm**.

3. If you **obsess** over minor details, you risk losing sight of the big picture.

4. Now that we know that this paper airplane design doesn't work, we will just have to **oust** a new one.

5. Today's rain boots are made of either rubber or plastic because these materials are not **porous**.

6. Does scientific evidence show that getting plenty of vitamin C in your diet will **bolster** your chances of avoiding a cold?

7. When the moon is bright and **prone**, it is much easier to see at night.

8. This workshop is highly recommended for those who would like to **deplore** their public speaking skills.

9. It will take weeks for the residents of the island to clean up the **residue** from the oil spill.

10. Some people regard superhero comic books as being shallow and **frivolous**, while others see them as significant expressions of modern myths.

Choosing the Right Word

*Select the **boldface** word that better completes each sentence. You might refer to the passage on pages 56–57 to see how most of these words are used in context. Note that the choices might be related forms of the Unit words.*

1. Only a person who is (**obsessed, bolstered**) with a desire to create beautiful music can become a great pianist or violinist.

2. I would not call Lucy a friend, as she made no (**qualms, residue**) about sharing your secret with everyone!

3. While my sister's memory is as retentive as a steel trap, mine seems to be as (**porous, staid**) as a sieve.

4. I like jokes as much as anyone, but I don't approve of making such (**frivolous, staid**) remarks when a serious matter is under discussion.

5. The way the witness blushed and stuttered when questioned (**ousted, bolstered**) my suspicions that he was not telling the truth.

6. After the claims of all the creditors have been satisfied, the (**residue, qualms**) of the estate will be shared by the children.

7. It is all very well to criticize and (**bolster, deplore**) the mistakes of young people, but why don't you also give them credit for their good qualities?

8. After being the apple of her eye for years, I suddenly found myself (**ousted, deplored**) from her affections by an upstart rival.

9. The team doctor ran onto the field toward the (**prone, frivolous**) figure of the injured football player.

10. After months of rejection, Leah decided to hire a professional manager, hoping to (**deplore, bolster**) her acting career.

11. We learned that behind the old professor's (**prone, staid**) exterior there was a keen wit and a lively sense of what life is all about.

12. I think that talking loudly on the phone in public so that everyone knows about your private life is (**deplorable, porous**) behavior.

Completing the Sentence

Choose the word from the word bank that best completes each of the following sentences. Write the correct word or form of the word in the space provided.

bolster	frivolous	oust	prone	residue
deplore	obsess	porous	qualm	staid

1. Because the villagers have so few dealings with the outside world, they are _____ to regard strangers with deep mistrust.

2. When we tried to carry water from the well, we found to our dismay that the bottom of the old bucket was _____.

3. Some people seem to have no _____ about manipulating others to gain their own ends.

4. Do not _____ about small details in your first draft of the essay, but address them in your revision.

5. When we heard about our teacher's serious illness, we visited him daily in the hospital to _____ his morale.

6. The two sisters are very different—one lively and fun-loving, the other quiet and rather _____.

7. I do not criticize people for trying to get ahead, but I _____ any attempt to take unfair advantage of others.

8. Certain saltlike chemicals may effectively prevent the streets from icing up in winter, but the powdery _____ they leave behind can damage footwear.

9. It is now time for you to take your work seriously and to give up some of the _____ activities of your earlier years.

10. Her public statements became so embarrassing that club members tried to _____ her from the presidency.

Definitions

Note the spelling, pronunciation, part(s) of speech, and definition(s) of each of the following words. Then write the appropriate form of the word in the blank space in the illustrative sentence(s) following.

1. annul
(ə nəl')

(*v.*) to reduce to nothing; to make ineffective or inoperative; to declare legally invalid or void

The state legislators voted by an overwhelming majority to _____ the out-of-date law.

2. blasé
(blä zā')

(*adj.*) indifferent, bored as a result of having enjoyed many pleasures; apathetic

Battle-hardened soldiers may tend to become a bit _____ about the dangers they face.

3. muster
(məs' tər)

(*v.*) to bring together for service or battle; to gather or summon; to amount to, comprise, include; (*n.*) a list of military personnel; a gathering, accumulation

You will need to _____ your courage to face the bully who has been tormenting you.

The sleepy new recruits assembled on the parade ground for the early morning _____.

4. nonentity
(nän en' tə tē)

(*n.*) a person or thing of no importance

We may not be movie stars, but we did not deserve to be treated as _____ by the presumptuous and haughty headwaiter.

5. ornate
(ôr nāt')

(*adj.*) elaborately decorated; showily splendid

If you ask me, an _____, gilded frame distracts the viewer's eye from a simple drawing.

6. peruse
(pə rüz')

(*v.*) to read thoroughly and carefully

It is wise to have a lawyer _____ an agreement before you sign it.

7. promontory
(präm' ən tôr ē)

(*n.*) a high point of land extending into water

We chose a high _____ overlooking the sea as the perfect spot for our picnic lunch.

8. recourse
(rē' kôrs)

(*n.*) a person or thing turned to for help or advice; the act of seeking help or protection

If my letter of complaint fails to get results, I will still have _____ to a higher authority.

9. solicitous
(sə lis′ ət əs)

(*adj.*) showing concern or care; fearful or anxious about someone or something

Neighbors made _____ inquiries about the state of the elderly couple's health.

10. sustain
(sə stān′)

(*v.*) to support, nourish, keep up; to suffer, undergo; to bear up under, withstand; to affirm the validity of

You may _____ a serious eye injury if you forget to wear your safety goggles when you work with chemicals or power tools.

Using Context

*For each item, determine whether the **boldface** word from pages 62–63 makes sense in the context of the sentence. Circle the item numbers next to the six sentences in which the words are used correctly.*

1. I opened the box to **peruse** the instructions before putting the furniture together, but I still could not understand what I was supposed to do.

2. The energy of the losing team only seemed to **muster** as the game went on, ensuring that they would not score enough points to win.

3. Because they had signed a lease saying they would pay rent for the next year, their only **recourse** to get out of the obligation early was to find a new tenant.

4. It's hard to believe that the now-famous chef was once a **nonentity** who had to beg people to taste his exotic recipes.

5. While new parents may try to soothe their newborns' every cry, parents of older children can sometimes seem **blasé** toward their toddlers' frequent tantrums.

6. I realized I would need to **annul** my speech in order to meet the five-minute minimum.

7. The house, usually decorated very simply, was almost unrecognizable due to the **ornate** decorations at the New Year's party.

8. She could not **sustain** such intense concentration for long periods of time, so she made sure to schedule some study breaks throughout the day.

9. The marathon winner stood on the **promontory** that was stationed by the finish line, holding up her medal for everyone to see.

10. His **solicitous** disregard for the well-being of everyone but himself can only be described as rude and unfeeling.

Choosing the Right Word

*Select the **boldface** word that better completes each sentence. You might refer to the passage on pages 56–57 to see how most of these words are used in context. Note that the choices might be related forms of the Unit words.*

1. Isn't it strange that a great American writer like Emily Dickinson was considered a (**nonentity, promontory**) in her own lifetime?

2. When the mile run began, Ken quickly took the lead, but we knew that he could not (**sustain, annul**) that pace for the entire race.

3. I admire the way Anne delivered a long, involved speech entirely without (**muster, recourse**) to written notes.

4. That wonderful woman could not have been more (**solicitous, ornate**) of me if she had been my own mother.

5. "It will take all the strength we can (**annul, muster**) to dislodge the enemy from that hill," the general observed grimly.

6. I hope someday to build a house on that (**nonentity, promontory**) commanding a beautiful view of the bay.

7. Because they failed to deliver the goods on time, we felt justified in (**annulling, perusing**) the entire contract.

8. My brother tried to appear (**blasé, ornate**) when he was named to the honor society, but I know that he was thrilled.

9. The novelist is known for her (**solicitous, ornate**) writing style, using many unusual words, figures of speech, and involved constructions.

10. If you want to learn to play chess, I suggest that you begin by (**sustaining, perusing**) a summary of the rules.

11. The young actor's (**ornate, blasé**) manner covered how excited and humble he felt when he won the Best Actor award.

12. When the war began, the country began to (**sustain, muster**) an army of all healthy citizens between 18 and 40 years of age.

Completing the Sentence

Choose the word from the word bank that best completes each of the following sentences. Write the correct word or form of the word in the space provided.

annul	muster	ornate	promontory	solicitous
blasé	nonentity	peruse	recourse	sustain

1. She is the kind of __solicitous__ teacher who aids and encourages her students in every way she can.

2. "In that barren wasteland," the explorer said, "we had great difficulty finding enough food to __sustain__ life."

   ran out of ink

3. There I was—an utter __nonentity__ in a group of famous and accomplished persons!

4. The furnishings in their house are so __ornate__ that the place looks more like a museum than a family home.

5. When my cousin returned home after his first year in college, he tried to impress us with his sophisticated and __blasé__ manner.

6. If you feel that you have been cheated, your only __recourse__ is to make a complaint to the department of consumer affairs in your city.

7. You should __peruse__ the instructions with great care before you fill out your application for admission.

8. A lighthouse was built on the tip of the __promontory__, where it served as a beacon for ships many miles away.

9. Every able-bodied citizen will be __mustered__ into active military service to fight off the invading force.

10. I will not allow a single act of carelessness to __annul__ the results of years of hard work.

Synonyms

*Choose the word or form of the word from this Unit that is the same or most nearly the same in meaning as the **boldface** word or expression in the phrase. Write that word on the line. Use a dictionary if necessary.*

1. scrubbed away the lime **deposit** _____
2. chose an **intricate** silverware pattern _____
3. have no **alternative** but to sue for damages _____
4. special exercises to **maintain** muscle tone _____
5. **detest** the creation of the atom bomb _____
6. dismissed the **petty** lawsuit _____
7. was **preoccupied** with thoughts of food when dieting _____
8. was **concerned** about my well-being _____
9. had no **misgivings** about taking the child's milk money _____
10. to be regarded as an **unknown** _____
11. will **pore over** the instructions before assembling the bed _____
12. may **strengthen** your ability to resist colds _____
13. resisted efforts to **overthrow** the monarchy _____
14. **apt** to take unnecessary chances _____
15. the spectacular view from the **headland** _____

Antonyms

*Choose the word or form of the word from this Unit that is most nearly opposite in meaning to the **boldface** word or expression in the phrase. Write that word on the line. Use a dictionary if necessary.*

1. designing a slick, **waterproof** fabric _____
2. **validate** the contract _____
3. **enthusiastic** about new experiences _____
4. **disband** the troops _____
5. wore a tie with a **gaudy** pattern _____

Writing: Words in Action

Suppose you were going to write a story about social injustice. What would you write about? What would be the outcome of your story? Write a brief synopsis of your story, including its theme. Use at least two details from the passage (pages 56–57), prior knowledge, and three or more words from this Unit.

Vocabulary in Context

*Some of the words you have studied in this Unit appear in **boldface** type. Read the passage below, and then circle the letter of the correct answer for each word as it is used in context.*

For students of the American theater, the landmark year 1959 is like a **promontory** on a rugged coastline. It marked the first production on Broadway of a play by an African American woman. The author was Lorraine Hansberry. The play was *A Raisin in the Sun*.

Hansberry borrowed her title from the poem "Harlem" by Langston Hughes, published eight years before, in 1951.The speaker in the poem, perhaps afraid of being dismissed as a **nonentity**, wonders what may happen to a dream that is deferred or postponed. Does such a dream wither, he muses, or does it possibly explode? Hughes suggests that opportunity can no longer be deferred. American society must become more open, equal, and just.

Likewise, the characters in Hansberry's acclaimed play dream of boosting their lives within a newly **porous** society. They strive to **annul** the **residue** and constraints of economic oppression and segregation.

In 1959, Hansberry's working-class African American characters captured the public imagination. There was nothing **ornate** about their speech or their surroundings. Their dreams, however, were clearly recognizable as consistent with the American Dream. For more than half a century, Hansberry's drama has been reenacted in sequels, Broadway revivals, films, television dramas, radio plays, and at least one musical. In 2014, *A Raisin in the Sun* made a triumphant return to Broadway. Tragically, Lorraine Hansberry witnessed few of her play's astonishing reincarnations. Her early death in 1965 cut short her richly promising career.

---

1. What is the meaning of **promontory** as it is used in paragraph 1?

a. peninsula   c. outcrop
b. fortress   d. gully

2. What does the use of the word **nonentity** suggest about the speaker's feelings?

a. He is afraid of being belittled.
b. He hopes to be remembered.
c. He is glad to be prosperous.
d. He feels betrayed.

3. The word **porous** means about the same as

a. permeable   c. prosperous
b. tolerant   d. resolute

4. Annul comes from the Latin word **annullare. Annullare** most likely means

a. to assert   c. to promote
b. to reject   d. to cancel

5. Which word means the same as **residue** as it is used in paragraph 3?

a. outsiders   c. liars
b. remains   d. complainers

6. What does **ornate** most likely mean as it is used in paragraph 4?

a. false   c. fancy
b. relevant   d. artificial

*Read the following passage, taking note of the **boldface** words and their contexts. These words are among those you will be studying in Unit 5. It may help you to complete the exercises in this Unit if you refer to the way the words are used below.*

Reality Check
<Persuasive Essay>

Can we please write an **epitaph** for reality TV? It's been a controversial, even **volatile** issue since the very first reality shows appeared. Are the programs harmless escapism and fun, as their many fans claim? Or are they mean-spirited, vulgar displays that deserve our **disdain**? Some believe there is **ample** evidence that reality TV is contributing to the dumbing down of America.

Let's get real: Reality TV isn't going away any time soon, and reality programs, whether they're off-the-wall dramas or over-the-top competitions, are massive money makers that **pulverize** competing shows in the ratings. It's not **plausible** that TV executives will pull the plug on their cash cows.

But reality shows are proliferating at an alarming rate. More and more outrageous scenarios and crazy ideas—often aimed at the most **plebeian** tastes—are being given the green light. Standards are at an all-time low. Show directors create contrived situations—"Let's send the cast to Italy and unleash our 'heroes' on an unsuspecting populace!" or "Let's put a bunch of troubled people in **proximity** and see what happens!" Some programs are clearly **facetious** and lighthearted, but others leave us shaking our heads at the producers' **indiscriminate** lack of judgment, good taste, and values.

Meanwhile, reality shows that pit people against each other can be downright cruel. Participants are required to undergo

Reality show devotees argue that there's nothing wrong with giving people what they want. Others make the case that only snobs put down reality TV—and they can always change channels if they don't like what's on. But when more people tune in to watch a reality star get married than watch the nightly news, or when more people can name the cast of a reality show than can name their own state's senators, our society is in *big* trouble.

We're experiencing reality overload, and it is time for a reality check. The Federal Communications Commission should **assert** its **jurisdiction** and put the brakes on the worst aspects of reality TV. Proponents of free speech might be **aghast**, but the national freak show needs to be tamed!

humiliating trials and perform risky stunts as they vie for cash and prizes. We watch contestants **cower** in fear as they confront writhing snakes, poisonous spiders, and other terrifying things. Or we cringe as they break down in tears in reaction to verbal abuse hurled at them by egotistical experts. Viewers are left wondering if the unprincipled show creators have an **ethical** bone in their bodies.

Just how real *are* these people and their adventures? Evidence indicates some shows are scripted, or at least mapped out ahead of time. It's pretty obvious that most are playing to the camera. Ordinary people become instant celebrities, but they're often exploited by the media and don't know how to handle their fame. The message is faulty: You don't have to work hard or be talented to achieve success; you just need to land on a reality show. It's not that easy—they're living in a fool's paradise.

As for "rehab" shows: Watching minor celebrities (or "D-listers") act out like toddlers and throw tantrums and scheme is like watching a train wreck in slo-mo—we can't turn away. There's **intrigue**! It's addictive! Just be sure to come back after the commercial break to see the next shocking and outlandish revelation!

Definitions

Note the spelling, pronunciation, part(s) of speech, and definition(s) of each of the following words. Then write the appropriate form of the word in the blank space in the illustrative sentence(s) following.

1. **addendum**
   (ə den′ dəm)

   (*n.*) a thing that is added; an appendix or addition to a book or written document
   The woman amended her will with an _____ when her husband suddenly died.

2. **aghast**
   (ə gast′)

   (*adj.*) filled with amazement, disgust, fear, or terror
   People were _____ at the senseless brutality of the crime.

3. **cower**
   (kaů′ ər)

   (*v.*) to crouch or shrink away in fear or shame
   The kittens _____ in the corner, frightened by the huge, growling dog.

4. **epitaph**
   (ep′ ə taf)

   (*n.*) a brief statement written on a tomb or gravestone
   Most people never stop to consider the words that might one day appear as their own _____.

5. **ethical**
   (eth′ ə kəl)

   (*adj.*) having to do with morals, values, right and wrong; in accordance with standards of right conduct; requiring a prescription for purchase
   New developments in medicine often lead to discussions of important _____ questions.

6. **inaudible**
   (in ô′ də bəl)

   (*adj.*) not able to be heard
   Some high-frequency sounds are _____ to even the keenest human ear.

7. **intrigue**
   (*n.*, in′ trēg;
   v., in trēg′)

   (*n.*) crafty dealings, underhanded plotting; (*v.*) to form and carry out plots; to puzzle or excite the curiosity
   Investigators uncovered a shocking network of lies and international _____.
   The old album full of faded family pictures and postcards from exotic places _____ me.

8. **plausible**
   (plô′ zə bəl)

   (*adj.*) appearing true, reasonable, or fair
   Their story didn't sound _____ to me.

9. prodigal
(präd′ ə gəl)

(*adj.*) wastefully extravagant; lavishly or generously abundant; (*n.*) one who is wasteful and self-indulgent

We have a tight budget, but we make an exception for _____ celebrations of family birthdays.

The elderly man told us that he greatly regretted the years he spent living the life of a _____.

10. volatile
(väl′ ə təl)

(*adj.*) highly changeable, fickle; tending to become violent or explosive; changing readily from the liquid to the gaseous state

A person who is usually calm may nevertheless sometimes behave in a _____ manner.

Using Context

*For each item, determine whether the **boldface** word from pages 70–71 makes sense in the context of the sentence. Circle the item numbers next to the six sentences in which the words are used correctly.*

1. Viewers watch the popular show to follow the **intrigue** and plot twists that will be revealed.

2. The lawyer will prepare an **addendum** for the contract and then send it to both parties.

3. It was difficult to read the old letter because the handwriting in it was so **inaudible**.

4. It would be **prodigal** to spend hundreds of dollars on fresh flowers for the party when we could easily make our own decorations.

5. I stopped and froze in place when I saw a snake suddenly **cower** across my path.

6. We were surprised to learn that the English poet Lord Byron wrote a lovely and moving **epitaph** for his dog, Boatswain, who died on November 18, 1808.

7. Young children often believe that **ethical** creatures, such as unicorns and dragons, exist.

8. The building of the Egyptian pyramids is generally recognized as one of the most **plausible** achievements of the ancient world.

9. The car owner was **aghast** to see that a huge tree had fallen on his vehicle during the storm.

10. People fear that the situation has become so **volatile** that war could break out at any time.

Choosing the Right Word

*Select the **boldface** word that better completes each sentence. You might refer to the passage on pages 68–69 to see how most of these words are used in context. Note that the choices might be related forms of the Unit words.*

1. It takes a practiced eye to make out the (**epitaphs, addendums**) on old, weather-beaten tombstones in a country churchyard.

2. His explanation that he is failing math because "the teacher is down on me" doesn't seem (**plausible, volatile**).

3. One of the most (**intriguing, prodigal**) mysteries I have ever read involved a priest and was set in the Wild West.

4. It will take the two of us months of strict economizing to make up for this one weekend of (**ethical, prodigal**) shopping.

5. The voters, (**volatile, aghast**) that such scandal could occur in their town, demanded the mayor's immediate resignation.

6. Her moods are so (**inaudible, volatile**) that we never know if she will be in a good humor or down in the dumps.

7. Lawyers may be punished by disbarment if it can be shown that they have violated the (**ethics, epitaphs**) of the legal profession.

8. The tenant wanted the landlord to include a mold (**epitaph, addendum**) in his lease so the owner would be responsible for any mold problems.

9. Government officials believe the pirate situation occurring in the high seas remains (**inaudible, volatile**) and requires immediate action.

10. You can show respect for your supervisors without seeming to (**intrigue, cower**) whenever one of them speaks to you.

11. I thought that my whispers to you were (**prodigal, inaudible**), but I learned otherwise when the teacher told me in no uncertain terms to be quiet.

12. I find my friend's stories about life in her native country most (**volatile, intriguing**).

Completing the Sentence

Choose the word from the word bank that best completes each of the following sentences. Write the correct word or form of the word in the space provided.

addendum	cower	ethical	intrigue	prodigal
aghast	epitaph	inaudible	plausible	volatile

1. Because the P.A. system was not working, the voice of the speaker was completely _____ to most of the people in the hall.

2. Did Ben Jonson write the _____ engraved on Shakespeare's tombstone?

3. Although they did not dare to attack the emperor publicly, they _____ in secret to bring about his downfall.

4. The way the child _____ around Rex gave me the impression that he had a fear of dogs.

5. I appreciate your _____ display of gratitude, but a simple "thank you" would do.

6. Notes from a rare interview were included as a(n) _____ in the second edition of the comedian's biography.

7. For the moment the crowd was quiet and subdued, but we knew that it was so _____ that it might become ugly and dangerous at any time.

8. The writer of the mystery story set up an interesting situation, but in my opinion the ending was not _____.

9. People of all religions strive to live up to high moral and _____ standards.

10. Observers on the ground were _____ to see the rocket explode and plunge back to earth seconds after launch.

Definitions

Note the spelling, pronunciation, part(s) of speech, and definition(s) of each of the following words. Then write the appropriate form of the word in the blank space in the illustrative sentence(s) following.

1. ample
(am′ pəl)

(*adj.*) more than enough, large, spacious
Thanks to the wet spring weather, birds and other animals will have an _____ food supply for the rest of the year.

2. apparition
(ap ə rish′ ən)

(*n.*) a ghost or ghostly figure; an unexplained or unusual appearance
The vivid _____ seemed so real that it completely unnerved me.

3. assert
(ə sərt′)

(*v.*) to declare or state as truth, maintain or defend, put forward forcefully
Throughout the trial and the lengthy appeal process that followed, the defendant _____ her innocence.

4. disdain
(dis dān′)

(*v.*) to look upon with scorn; to refuse scornfully; (*n.*) a feeling of contempt
I _____ their cowardly behavior.
Fair-minded people feel _____ for racism.

5. facetious
(fə sē′ shəs)

(*adj.*) humorous, not meant seriously
We had to laugh at her _____ remarks.

6. indiscriminate
(in dis krim′ ə nət)

(*adj.*) without restraint or control; unselective
The _____ slaughter of white whales brought that species to the brink of extinction.

7. jurisdiction
(jür is dik′ shən)

(*n.*) an area of authority or control; the right to administer justice
Cases involving robbery and assault are usually tried under the _____ of the state courts.

8. plebeian
(plə bē′ ən)

(*adj.*) common, vulgar; belonging to the lower class; (*n.*) a common person, member of the lower class
The couple's taste in cars is quite _____.
At one time, the _____ of ancient Rome were excluded from holding public office of any kind.

9. **proximity**
   (präk sim′ ə tē)

(*n.*) nearness, closeness

The house's _____ to schools is an asset.

10. **pulverize**
    (pəl′ və rīz)

(*v.*) to grind or pound to a powder or dust; to destroy or overcome (as though by smashing into fragments)

At many old mills in Vermont, granite stones were used to _____ the grain.

Using Context

*For each item, determine whether the **boldface** word from pages 74–75 makes sense in the context of the sentence. Circle the item numbers next to the six sentences in which the words are used correctly.*

1. The teacher made clear not only the school's policy about cheating, but also her personal **disdain** for those who try to pass off others' work as their own.

2. Since my father once missed his flight due to being stuck in traffic, he now always makes sure we have **ample** time to get to the airport.

3. Her dry sense of humor makes it hard to tell when she is serious and when she is being **facetious**.

4. The cat's dislike of the dog was made clear when she put as much **proximity** between herself and the other animal as possible while still remaining in the house.

5. I attempted to **assert** her statement by listing all of the facts that would prove her wrong, but she simply ignored me.

6. The boy's **indiscriminate** appetite means that he will eat nearly anything you put in front of him.

7. The reporter made clear that he was only responsible for what he wrote and had no **jurisdiction** over anything else that would be published in the magazine.

8. Although he was nervous to compete in the race, the proud faces of his family in the crowd were enough to **pulverize** his spirits and encourage him to win first place.

9. Her vast record collection shows her **plebeian** taste in music, with genres ranging from classical to heavy metal.

10. I woke up to what appeared to be an **apparition** floating just outside my window, only to turn on the light and see that it was a tree branch blowing in the wind.

Choosing the Right Word

Select the **boldface** word that better completes each sentence. You might refer to the passage on pages 68–69 to see how most of these words are used in context. Note that the choices might be related forms of the Unit words.

1. I wonder how many asteroids Superman could (**disdain, pulverize**) with his bare hands.

2. In Shakespeare's *Macbeth*, the witches show the title character three prophetic (**jurisdictions, apparitions**).

3. Your thoughtless remarks hurt me deeply, even though you say that you were merely trying to be (**indiscriminate, facetious**).

4. Only a snob would show such (**disdain, proximity**) for someone who doesn't drive a fancy car.

5. Deciding who is or isn't eligible for school athletic teams is not within the (**proximity, jurisdiction**) of the student council.

6. Sometimes it is difficult to tell if my brother is being (**facetious, plebeian**) or if he really means the things he says.

7. I do not believe that people who come from poor families should be regarded as (**apparitions, plebeians**).

8. The purpose of this experiment is to find out whether a substance will dissolve more rapidly in water if it is thoroughly (**asserted, pulverized**).

9. In recent decades, we have been forced to make greater use of our (**ample, plebeian**) coal supply to meet our growing energy needs.

10. The (**proximity, jurisdiction**) of the leaders' ideas on many subjects made it easy for them to work together during that critical period of our history.

11. My neighbor's furniture is supposed to be "original" and "colorful," but I think it is a(n) (**indiscriminate, facetious**) collection of junk.

12. Although I may not agree with what you have to say, I will always (**assert, disdain**) your right to say it.

Completing the Sentence

Choose the word from the word bank that best completes each of the following sentences. Write the correct word or form of the word in the space provided.

| ample | assert | facetious | jurisdiction | proximity |
| apparition | disdain | indiscriminate | plebeian | pulverize |

1. The "ghostly figure" you think you saw in the graveyard was no more than a(n) _____ created by your imagination.

2. I hope he was just being _____ when he said that my dancing reminded him of a trained bear.

3. A(n) _____ TV viewer, who watches any program, good or bad, is bound to waste a lot of time.

4. In answer to unfair criticisms, we proudly _____ that our family has always been generous in its aid to the needy.

5. The planning board refused to allow the construction of a factory in close _____ to our school building.

6. Regulation of radio and TV stations falls within the _____ of the federal government.

7. Since you were given _____ time to prepare your report, I can see no excuse for your failure to complete it.

8. The giant crushers lifted the boulders and quickly _____ them into a uniform gray powder.

9. Who would be so proud or so foolish as to _____ a helping hand in time of real need?

10. In that elegant French restaurant, which serves all kinds of fancy foods, she ordered a(n) _____ ham and cheese on rye.

Synonyms

*Choose the word or form of the word from this Unit that is the same or most nearly the same in meaning as the **boldface** word or expression in the phrase. Write that word on the line. Use a dictionary if necessary.*

1. terrified by **spirits**   _____
2. **mystified** by their unusual behavior   _____
3. has **considerable** room to move in this large space   _____
4. show **contempt** for intolerance   _____
5. **cringed** as the tornado whirled past   _____
6. the clearest way to **pronounce** our freedom   _____
7. remarks came across as **comical**   _____
8. **unrefined** taste in music   _____
9. not considered **honorable** to cheat on a test   _____
10. known to have a highly **unpredictable** disposition   _____
11. the **haphazard** assaults on his own citizens   _____
12. moved by the words on the **tombstone inscription**   _____
13. **crushed** turquoise to use as paint pigment   _____
14. under the **authorization** of the United Nations   _____
15. a letter that includes a **postscript**   _____

Antonyms

*Choose the word or form of the word from this Unit that is most nearly opposite in meaning to the **boldface** word or expression in the phrase. Write that word on the line. Use a dictionary if necessary.*

1. made a reply that was **easily heard**   _____
2. offered us a **far-fetched** alibi   _____
3. a person with **thrifty** spending habits   _____
4. **delighted** by his behavior at the tranquil ceremony   _____
5. **distance** of my job from home   _____

Writing: Words in Action

Suppose you are a TV executive and have been receiving complaints about a particular reality show. The show's ratings are good, and it is inexpensive to produce. Write an argument deciding whether to keep the show or replace it. Use at least two details from the passage (pages 68–69) and three or more words from the Unit.

Vocabulary in Context

*Some of the words you have studied in this Unit appear in **boldface** type. Read the passage below, and then circle the letter of the correct answer for each word as it is used in context.*

In many contemporary homes, tablets, televisions, smartphones, laptops, and computers have become a **prodigal** expenditure. Screens, with their bright characters and interactive features, **intrigue** children and adults alike. Children, however, should not be exposed to screens as much as adults. Therefore, pediatricians have set guidelines for how much screen time is recommended for children. The American Academy of Pediatrics defines screen time as any time spent using digital media for entertainment purposes. Previously, the American Academy of Pediatrics established a general screen time limit of two hours for all children over the age of two. In 2016, they released an **addendum** to these guidelines.

The new recommendations state that babies under 18 months are the most vulnerable to screens, even if the volume is **inaudible**. Babies find **ample** stimulation in the regular world, and screens can overwhelm them. Therefore, pediatricians do not recommend screen time for babies. For children ages two to five, the Academy recommends a limit of one hour per day. This limit allows parents to encourage more creative play. For children six and older, pediatricians assert that screen time is dependent on the child and family. They agree that parents should encourage children to use screen time positively since homework can be completed on screens. Parents should also take their children's individual personalities into account. For example, children who are overly sensitive should avoid watching a scary movie with an **apparition.** Regardless of the child or the family, pediatricians believe screens should never replace interpersonal interactions between parents and children.

---

1. What is the meaning of **prodigal** as it is used in paragraph 1?
   a. important
   b. limited
   c. extravagant
   d. impersonal

2. The word **intrigue** means about the same as
   a. excite curiosity
   b. remain constant
   c. state arguments
   d. provoke anger

3. Which word means the same as **addendum** as it is used in paragraph 1?
   a. substitution
   b. addition
   c. comparison
   d. analysis

4. What is the meaning of **inaudible** as it is used in paragraph 2?
   a. not able to be eaten
   b. not able to be felt
   c. not able to be used
   d. not able to be heard

5. Ample comes from the Latin word **amplus. Amplus** most likely means
   a. direct
   b. partial
   c. abundant
   d. real

6. What does **apparition** most likely mean as it is used in paragraph 2?
   a. omen
   b. warning
   c. soundtrack
   d. ghost

Read the following passage, taking note of the **boldface** words and their contexts. These words are among those you will be studying in Unit 6. It may help you to complete the exercises in this Unit if you refer to the way the words are used below.

Diary of a Young Migrant Worker
<Diary Entry>

All the children worked, here as cotton laborers in Arizona, 1937.

This is a fictional diary of 12-year-old Eldora Soto Vega, a Mexican-American girl in a family of migrant farmworkers in California in 1940. The family lived in temporary camps and moved from farm to farm to follow seasonal work, picking crops.

September 15, 1940

We are now on an enormous farm in the San Joaquin Valley, picking cotton. My brother Emilio is back after picking grapes in Napa. The long, hot days in the fields picking avocados and cantaloupes made us tired, because we started at five in the morning! The Anglos **ostracize** *campesinos,* and we stay in our own camps, sometimes living near an irrigation ditch. We use the ditch water for all our needs, and Mamá said this is why many get sick. The other farmworkers don't live like kings, but at least their camps have toilets and running water.

October 5, 1940

A few of the Anglo kids around here are nice, but most are **aloof** and ignore us, and some are just plain mean. I am jealous of a girl who **flaunts** her new jacket, **basking** in compliments, while my shoes are two sizes too small. My mother called California "the Land of Milk and Honey," but I am more **forthright:** How can such a bountiful place be so cruel? We are **scapegoats** when anything goes wrong—like yesterday,

People worked long hours under the hot sun for little pay.

Some families were lucky enough to have their own car. Here, stranded migrants in 1936 California wait for help.

one of the bushels of cotton went missing. The foreman blamed my father, but we all know it was the foreman's nephew who misplaced it.

November 8, 1940

We are camped at another farm 20 miles north, picking peas. The rain is leaking through our shack's roof of burlap and palm leaves and onto my diary. It's one of the many **defects** of our little dwelling, but at least the rain gives us a chance to rest. My name, Eldora, means "golden," and Papá said he wanted to **instill** pride in me by giving me a name with significance. I try to remember that when I see signs like this one at the park: "For White People Only. Mexicans and Filipinos Keep Out."

December 1, 1940

Our **genial** neighbor, Señora Medina, has set up a *taqueria* for the workers. She is getting a little old for fieldwork, but she wants to help the community, for in time of test, family is best. There was only enough corn dough for one taco each, and I am **abashed** to admit I took a second one. Señor Medina caught me, and I'm scared of **repercussions**, so I'll hide until things blow over!

December 6, 1940

I heard Mamá telling Papá she had a **premonition** something terrible would happen, and she was right. Our old car broke down, and now it's propped up on bricks because Papá sold the tires. Mamá tries to hide her **anguish,** but she is worried, because we can be "repatriated" to Mexico at any time, especially if we can no longer get from place to place. We were all born here, but we have no papers to prove it, and many others have already been sent back in a **purge** of Mexican and Mexican American workers. Officials say they want to keep the few jobs for "real" Americans. That's why Papá won't join a strike, even though he agrees with the strikers, because he can't risk being arrested.

December 20, 1940

Everyone says to stop dreaming, but I am **resolute**—when I am grown, I will have a little house, and it will be more than a shack made out of cardboard boxes. I will have a garden, too. And I will go to school, and my children will not have to work like my brothers and sisters and I must.

Audio

For iWords and audio passages, go to SadlierConnect.com.

Definitions

Note the spelling, pronunciation, part(s) of speech, and definition(s) of each of the following words. Then write the appropriate form of the word in the blank space in the illustrative sentence(s) following.

1. **abashed**
   (ə basht′)

   (*adj., part.*) embarrassed, ashamed, or nonplussed
   I was thoroughly _____ by
   the foolish mistake I made at the dinner party.

2. **articulate**
   (*v.,* är tik′ yü lāt;
   adj., är tik′ yə lit)

   (*v.*) to pronounce distinctly; to express well in words;
   to fit together into a system; (*adj.*) able to use language
   effectively; expressed clearly and forcefully
   A successful candidate can _____
   ideas in a way that makes them acceptable to voters.
   To be successful as a professional lecturer, a person
   must, of necessity, be _____.

3. **defect**
   (*n.,* dē′ fekt;
   v., di fekt′)

   (*n.*) an imperfection, flaw, or blemish of some
   kind; (*v.*) to desert a cause or organization
   There is no one who does not have at least
   one serious character _____.
   In 1948 the Dixiecrats, a group of Southern Democrats,
   _____ from the Democratic Party and
   held their own presidential nominating convention.

4. **flaunt**
   (flônt)

   (*v.*) to wave or flutter showily; to display in a
   conceited, offensive way
   Some people seem to need to _____
   their wealth and good fortune in life.

5. **genial**
   (jēn′ yəl)

   (*adj.*) cordial, pleasantly cheerful or warm
   The _____ host and hostess
   made each party guest feel especially welcome.

6. **ostracize**
   (äs′ trə sīz)

   (*v.*) to exclude from a group, banish, send away
   Society _____ those who commit
   acts of treason.

7. **premonition**
   (prē mə nish′ ən)

   (*n.*) forewarning or foreboding of a future event
   I felt a vague _____ of danger as
   I entered the abandoned building.

8. repercussion
(rē pər kəsh′ ən)

(*n.*) an effect or consequence of some action or event, result; an echo or reverberation

The _____ of the 1929 stock market crash were felt all over the world.

9. retentive
(ri tent′ iv)

(*adj.*) able to hold, keep, or recall; retaining knowledge easily

A _____ memory is a great asset for any actor.

10. scapegoat
(skāp′ gōt)

(*n.*) a person or thing carrying the blame for others

In ancient times, a messenger who brought bad news was often made the _____ for it and killed.

Using Context

*For each item, determine whether the **boldface** word from pages 82–83 makes sense in the context of the sentence. Circle the item numbers next to the six sentences in which the words are used correctly.*

1. In a few weeks that clumsy-looking caterpillar will **flaunt** into a beautiful butterfly.

2. I ignored the **abashed** bragging of my competitor and kept a focused determination.

3. Engineers will determine whether a mechanical **defect** caused the rocket to explode.

4. Some people are naturally **articulate**, while others must work to find the right words.

5. The **genial** storeowner knows most of her customers by name.

6. Lifting weights is a good way to **ostracize** both your muscles and your bones.

7. The pirates were wrong to believe that they could seize the king's ships and take the crews prisoner without **repercussion**.

8. This glass window is so **retentive** that it can withstand a heavy blow without cracking.

9. The lawyer argued that his client was merely a **scapegoat** and promised to expose the people who had actually stolen the funds.

10. The innkeeper predicted that the travellers would have a long and difficult journey, but fortunately his **premonition** did not come true.

Choosing the Right Word

*Select the **boldface** word that better completes each sentence. You might refer to the passage on pages 80–81 to see how most of these words are used in context. Note that the choices might be related forms of the Unit words.*

1. It was shocking how quickly the singer was (**ostracized, defected**) for voicing her opinions about free speech.

2. Jefferson preferred to (**articulate, defect**) his ideas about government and religion in writing rather than give public speeches.

3. Fortunately, the soil is so (**abashed, retentive**) of moisture that the weeks of dry weather did not damage our crops.

4. The new governor's address was an unusually (**articulate, abashed**) and effective description of the challenges facing the state in the years ahead.

5. His prejudices are so strong that he wants to (**ostracize, flaunt**) all members of minority religious groups.

6. How can we ever forgive him for (**defecting, articulating**) from our great cause at the very time we needed him most?

7. It would be good taste on his part not to (**flaunt, ostracize**) all the honors and awards that he has won.

8. She is not the most (**articulate, genial**) person in the world, but in her own way she is at least trying to be friendly.

9. It will be better if we all take responsibility for the mistake instead of letting one employee be the (**premonition, scapegoat**).

10. The college student did not understand the serious (**premonitions, repercussions**) of plagiarism when he downloaded an essay from the Internet.

11. Shakespeare tries to convey Brutus's (**defects, premonitions**) of defeat at Philippi by having Caesar's ghost appear to him the night before the battle.

12. Although he was trying to look unconcerned, I could see that he was much (**abashed, retentive**) by the teacher's criticism.

Completing the Sentence

Choose the word from the word bank that best completes each of the following sentences. Write the correct word or form of the word in the space provided.

abashed	defect	genial	premonition	retentive
articulate	flaunt	ostracize	repercussion	scapegoat

1. Although Hal was the only boy at the formal dance wearing sneakers and an old sweatshirt, he did not seem at all _____.

2. Although every form of government has its _____, democracy has more pluses and fewer minuses than any other.

3. I criticize him not because he makes mistakes but because he constantly looks for a(n) _____ to take the blame for them.

4. She has such a(n) _____ mind that she seems able to master complicated details without even taking notes.

5. Since we all know that you sing and play the piano beautifully, what need is there for you to _____ your musical talents?

6. The defendant was found not guilty at his trial, but his punishment came when he was _____ by all his friends.

7. We learned that beneath the old man's quiet and withdrawn manner, there was a charming and _____ personality.

8. In recent years, pollution of our waterways has had serious and sometimes fatal _____ on the wildlife that inhabits them.

9. Even though I assured my friend that I would visit him when he moved abroad, I had a strange _____ that I would never see him again.

10. The speaker could not be understood easily because he swallowed his words instead of _____ them clearly.

Definitions

Note the spelling, pronunciation, part(s) of speech, and definition(s) of each of the following words. Then write the appropriate form of the word in the blank space in the illustrative sentence(s) following.

1. aloof
(ə lüf′)

(*adj.*) withdrawn, standing apart from others by choice

In almost every office or business, there are some people who keep decidedly _____ from their coworkers.

2. anguish
(aŋ′ gwish)

(*n.*) great mental suffering, distress, or pain; (*v.*) to cause deep pain or sorrow

Survivors of a natural disaster often suffer great mental _____ long after their terrible ordeal is over.

The child's disappearance _____ every member of the community.

3. bask
(bask)

(*v.*) to be in, or expose oneself to, pleasant warmth; to take pleasure in or derive enjoyment from

Because they are cold-blooded, lizards and other reptiles must _____ in the sun to regulate their body temperature.

4. finesse
(fi nes′)

(*n.*) delicate skill; tact and cleverness; (*v.*) to accomplish something by cleverness, good judgment, or skillful evasion

To become a champion, a tennis player needs to combine power with _____.

Skilled politicians know how to _____ their answers to embarrassing questions from reporters.

5. forthright
(fôrth′ rīt)

(*adj.*) frank, direct, straightforward

I appreciate the _____ way in which you express your opinions, even when they do not agree with my own.

6. instill
(in stil′)

(*v.*) to add gradually; to introduce or cause to be taken in

How can parents best _____ in their children a love for reading?

7. pseudonym
(sü′ də nim)

(*n.*) a pen name, name assumed by a writer

It is wise to use a _____ to protect your privacy when you chat on the Internet.

8. **purge**
(pərj)

(*v.*) to wash away impurities, clean up; (*n.*) the process of getting rid of something or someone decisively

A soaking rainstorm will usually _____ the air of pollutants.

The change of government was achieved through an election, not through a brutal _____.

9. **rehabilitate**
(rē hə bil' ə tāt)

(*v.*) to make over in good form; to restore to good condition or to a former position

Government agencies have spent sums of money trying to _____ run-down neighborhoods.

10. **resolute**
(rez' ə lüt)

(*adj.*) bold, determined; firm

Be _____ in pursuit of your dreams.

Using Context

*For each item, determine whether the **boldface** word from pages 86–87 makes sense in the context of the sentence. Circle the item numbers next to the six sentences in which the words are used correctly.*

1. After surgery, exercises helped me **rehabilitate** the muscles in my shoulder.

2. The author was excited to **bask** in the praise of his fans at the book signing.

3. The **anguish** I felt when I collapsed into bed after a long day was such a relief!

4. His social **finesse** makes him a hit at parties, as he is always engaged in lively conversation.

5. I was taught never to pet a dog or **instill** his food while he is eating it.

6. Many of my classmates thought the new student seemed **aloof**, but I suspect that he just did not want to seem overly eager to make friends.

7. The famous author decided to write her new series under a **pseudonym** so that people would not judge it against her previous work.

8. Her **resolute** response was so vague that we were even more confused than before.

9. I was determined to **purge** from my closet any clothes that I had not worn in over a year, but couldn't actually bring myself to throw anything out.

10. He was commended for his **forthright** behavior after risking his life to save a cat.

Choosing the Right Word

*Select the **boldface** word that better completes each sentence. You might refer to the passage on pages 80–81 to see how most of these words are used in context. Note that the choices might be related forms of the Unit words.*

1. Many female authors once used male (**purges, pseudonyms**) because it was considered improper for women to write novels.

2. We should now be just as (**forthright, resolute**) in fighting for peace as the Americans of 200 years ago were in fighting for independence.

3. An actor who has (**basked, instilled**) for so long in the favor of the public finds it hard to realize that he or she is no longer popular.

4. By teaching her son how to garden and fish, Hilary hoped to (**anguish, instill**) in him a love of nature.

5. She has lived (**aloof, forthright**) from other people for so long that it is hard for her to take part in everyday social affairs.

6. No matter how much time or effort it takes, I will (**purge, instill**) these unfair charges of disloyalty from my reputation!

7. Is it our duty to try to (**bask, instill**) a faith in democracy in the people of other lands?

8. Many people view cats as (**finesse, aloof**) and averse to cuddling.

9. The purpose of our prison system is not just to punish offenders but to (**finesse, rehabilitate**) them.

10. It is possible to be honest and (**forthright, aloof**) in stating your views and opinions without being cruel or tactless.

11. My (**anguish, finesse**) at the loss of a loved one was all the greater when I realized that my carelessness had caused the accident.

12. He's cleverly managed to (**rehabilitate, finesse**) his way into a very important position in this company.

Completing the Sentence

Choose the word from the word bank that best completes each of the following sentences. Write the correct word or form of the word in the space provided.

aloof	bask	forthright	pseudonym	rehabilitate
anguish	finesse	instill	purge	resolute

1. I have learned over the years that it is often possible to accomplish more by _____ than by brute force.

2. The city planner said that in addition to building new housing, we should plan to _____ many old buildings.

3. I think you will know who William S. Porter was if I tell you that he used the _____ O. Henry.

4. Instead of a(n) _____ answer, all we got from her was, "In one sense, yes, but on the other hand, perhaps no."

5. The star basketball player ___*basked*___ in the admiration of every small child in the neighborhood.

6. Good citizens don't remain _____ from the problems in their communities.

7. It took four years of civil war to _____ this nation of the curse of slavery.

8. By the example of their own conduct, our parents _____ in us a deep respect for people of all races, nationalities, and religions.

9. After the infamous attack on Pearl Harbor, the American people were ___*forthright*___ in their determination to defeat the fascist powers.

10. Our _____ turned to joy when the missing plane and its passengers landed safely.

Synonyms

*Choose the word or form of the word from this Unit that is the same or most nearly the same in meaning as the **boldface** word or expression in the phrase. Write that word on the line. Use a dictionary if necessary.*

1. a **watertight** vessel _____
2. **restores** antique cars as a hobby _____
3. **expel** the vermin from the house _____
4. likes to **show off** her expensive watch _____
5. on sale because of the **flaw** in the cookware _____
6. accepting praise with **poise** _____
7. **reveled** in the applause _____
8. an **amiable** and giving companion _____
9. had a **presentiment** of impending doom _____
10. remained **steadfast** in her opinion _____
11. gave **candid** answers to the prosecutor _____
12. a rather **standoffish** disposition _____
13. **snubbed** the newcomers _____
14. refuse to be made the **fall guy** again _____
15. **ingrain** in them a love of country _____

Antonyms

*Choose the word or form of the word from this Unit that is most nearly opposite in meaning to the **boldface** word or expression in the phrase. Write that word on the line. Use a dictionary if necessary.*

1. gave an **incoherent** statement to reporters _____
2. **unembarrassed** by the topic of discussion _____
3. the **cause** of global warming _____
4. watched with a look of **delight** _____
5. signed the book with his **real name** _____

Writing: Words in Action

What is the American Dream? How can it be attained? Is it achievable for all? Why or why not? In a brief essay, support your view with details and examples from the passage (pages 80–81), your studies, or personal experience. Use three or more words from this Unit.

Vocabulary in Context

*Some of the words you have studied in this Unit appear in **boldface** type. Read the passage below, and then circle the letter of the correct answer for each word as it is used in context.*

From the unique black-clay urns of Oaxaca to the colorful papier-mâché figures sold in the vibrant, **genial** markets of Mexico City, Mexican folk art is admired the world over. While many folk artists sell their wares to make a living, many also **articulate** the joy and satisfaction of the creative process.

And it *is* creative—and often thrifty too. When making their papier-mâché objects, for example, artisans first create an armature, or frame, often of cardboard or wire. Then they **rehabilitate** newspaper. They cut it into strips and apply layer after layer to the frame with a simple paste of water and flour. Once the layers are dry, the folk artists paint the objects and **finesse** the details.

Other popular folk arts of the country include weaving, jewelry making, metalwork, mosaics, and bark-paper painting. Each region has its own specialty, although all share a love of vibrant color. Most folk artists display their work proudly, signing their names, but there are likely a few who prefer to use a **pseudonym** to protect their privacy.

Many of Mexico's arts and crafts techniques stem from age-old traditions of the artists' Indian and Spanish ancestors. Older artists have a **retentive** memory of these practices, and pass them on to their children and grandchildren. In this way, traditions and artistry are kept alive. Mexico City has many charming folk art markets and the Museo de Arte Popular (Museum of Popular Art). It has an impressive collection of old and new folk art.

---

1. **Genial** comes from the Latin word **genialis. Genialis** most likely means
   a. gentle
   b. festive
   c. somber
   d. active

2. What is the meaning of **articulate** as it is used in paragraph 1?
   a. accept an offer
   b. convey in silence
   c. express in words
   d. barter for goods

3. What is the meaning of **rehabilitate** as it is used in paragraph 2?
   a. tear
   b. pack
   c. reduce
   d. reclaim

4. The word **finesse** means about the same as
   a. perfect with skill
   b. strengthen with paper
   c. cover with paint
   d. alter with inability

5. What does **pseudonym** most likely mean as it is used in paragraph 3?
   a. rubber stamp
   b. pen name
   c. false note
   d. real identity

6. Which word means the opposite of **retentive** as it is used in paragraph 4?
   a. flawed
   b. impeccable
   c. fortunate
   d. forgetful

Vocabulary for Comprehension
Part 1

Read "The Umbrella: A Portable Roof," which contains words in **boldface** *that appear in Units 4–6. Then answer the questions.*

The Umbrella: A Portable Roof

Most people probably take the umbrella for granted. Today, almost everyone has one. But there was a time when the umbrella was a rare possession reserved
(5) for royalty.

Umbrellas were first used for protection from the sun. In fact, the word *umbrella* comes from the Latin *umbra*, which means "shade." The umbrella made
(10) shade portable.

The earliest known depiction of an umbrella appears on a monument to a Mesopotamian king, Sargon of Akkad, that dates from about 2400 BCE. The
(15) king is shown leading his victorious army while a **solicitous** aide walks behind him, shading him with an umbrella. Umbrellas also appear in the art of ancient Egypt, Greece, India, Rome, and China.
(20) Everywhere, the umbrella was associated with the elite, not with **plebeians.**

Umbrellas made of paper were **porous** and therefore of little use as protection in stormy weather. During the Wei dynasty
(25) (386–535 CE), the Chinese devised an oiled-paper umbrella for use in sun or rain. The emperor's **ornate** umbrella was red and yellow, the royal colors. The ancient Romans also developed oiled-paper
(30) umbrellas. In the fourteenth century, weavers fashioned silk fabrics sturdy enough to use for umbrellas.

In 1340, a papal envoy to India wrote of a "little tent-roof on a cane handle," which
(35) the people "open out at will as a protection against sun or rain." The envoy brought an umbrella back to Italy. However, the device was slow to gain popularity in Europe, where it was considered a
(40) woman's accessory. Men would have been embarrassed to be seen using an umbrella, even in the heaviest downpour.

The umbrella did not catch on with men until around 1750, when a British gentleman
(45) named Jonas Hanway began carrying one almost every day. He **sustained** years of public ridicule for doing so. In 1778, John MacDonald endured similar disapproval. As these gentlemen strode by carrying
(50) their umbrellas, passersby and coachmen, **aghast**, mocked them. But eventually men became convinced that carrying an umbrella in rainy London was both stylish and practical. Before long, thanks to
(55) Hanway and MacDonald, no proper Englishman would be seen without a hat, gloves, and an umbrella. Often the handle of the umbrella even had a hidden compartment for storing small accessories,
(60) like a pad and a pencil.

Soon it became acceptable for everyone to use the umbrella. This popularity paved the way for innovations in umbrella design, and in 1852, the umbrella evolved from a
(65) ten-pound object with a long handle and heavy wax-coated cotton stretched over cane or whalebone rods to a lighter canopy with a steel frame.

1. Which sentence **best** states the author's purpose in the passage?
   A) The author explains the etymology of the word *umbrella*.
   B) The author entertains readers with fictional details about the umbrella.
   C) The author informs readers about the history of the umbrella.
   D) The author persuades readers to use umbrellas as protection from the sun.

2. What does the word **solicitous** most likely mean as it is used in line 16?
   A) attentive
   B) unconcerned
   C) smiling
   D) faithful

3. The word **plebeian** has more than one meaning. As used in line 21, what does the word **plebeians** most likely mean?
   A) common people
   B) vulgarities
   C) professionals
   D) aristocrats

4. Which statement is **best** supported by lines 11–14?
   A) Art from ancient Egypt shows that the first use of an umbrella occurred there.
   B) The word *umbrella* comes from the Latin *umbra*.
   C) Umbrellas were first used for protection from the rain.
   D) People have been using umbrellas for over 4,000 years.

5. What does the word **porous** in line 22 **most likely** suggest?
   A) Umbrellas were fragile.
   B) Umbrellas were durable.
   C) Umbrellas were permeable.
   D) Umbrellas were colorful.

6. Which word means the opposite of **ornate** in line 27?
   A) elegant
   B) simple
   C) ample
   D) elaborate

7. **Part A**
   As it is used in this passage, what does the word **sustained** (line 46) mean?
   A) attracted
   B) ignored
   C) nourished
   D) suffered

   Part B
   Which sentence from "The Umbrella: A Portable Roof" provides the **best** clue to the meaning of the word **sustained**?
   A) "brought an umbrella back to Italy" (lines 36–37)
   B) "considered a woman's accessory" (lines 39–40)
   C) "endured similar disapproval" (line 48)
   D) "a hidden compartment for storing small accessories" (lines 58–59)

8. Which word is closest in meaning to the word **aghast** as it is used in line 51?
   A) shocked
   B) concerned
   C) amused
   D) delighted

9. Which statement **best** provides an inference that is supported by "The Umbrella: A Portable Roof"?
   A) Umbrellas were in common use in Europe before they were used in Asia.
   B) In ancient times, only common people used umbrellas.
   C) Jonas Hanway and John MacDonald made the umbrella acceptable to men.
   D) Jonas Hanway and John MacDonald made the umbrella unpopular in Europe.

10. How does the author primarily structure "The Umbrella: A Portable Roof"?
    A) using spatial order
    B) in chronological order
    C) using cause–effect order
    D) in comparison–contrast order

Vocabulary for Comprehension

Part 2

*Read these passages, which contain words in **boldface** that appear in Units 4–6. Then choose the best answer to each question based on what is stated or implied in the passage(s). You may refer to the passages as often as necessary.*

Questions 1–10 are based on the following passages.

Passage 1

The 1920s, dubbed the "Jazz Age," saw the rise of a distinctively American art form, musicals. A musical is a theatrical production that is typically sentimental

(5) and amusing and has music, dancing, and dialogue. Numerous origins of the form have been identified, including vaudeville, pantomime, and comic opera.

The first musical to present a tightly

(10) integrated plot and music coordinated with the narrative was *Show Boat* (1927). This piece, with lyrics by Oscar Hammerstein and music by Jerome Kern, **flaunted** the genre. Hammerstein was to partner with

(15) composer Richard Rodgers on some of the greatest musicals in the repertory. Their partnership began with *Oklahoma!* (1943) and continued with *Carousel* (1945) and *South Pacific* (1949). Critics

(20) found few **defects** in these shows.

The 1950s witnessed two landmark musicals that became classics: *My Fair Lady* (1956) by Alan Jay Lerner and Frederick Loewe, and *West Side Story*

(25) (1958) by Leonard Bernstein and Stephen Sondheim.

Any **forthright** account would have to acknowledge a decline in the American musical after the late 1960s. However,

(30) Broadway occasionally hosts spectacular, long-running productions, such as *A Chorus Line* (1975), *Cats* (1981), *The Phantom of the Opera* (1986), and *The Lion King* (1997).

Passage 2

Besides the leading performers, who

(35) else contributes to a successful musical? Most musicals require **ample** numbers of talented people. The financial resources needed to **bolster** a show give the producer many a **qualm,** and producers

(40) must **muster** sufficient funds to employ at least four key individuals besides the actors.

One crucial artist is the choreographer. In 1943, Rodgers and Hammerstein's *Oklahoma!* marked a milestone.

(45) Choreographer Agnes de Mille was the first to cast her own dancers; in prior musicals, producers had **recourse** to a system based on the dancers' looks instead of technical skills, but de Mille

(50) brought professional dancers to the fore.

The set designer also has a crucial role. This artist creates a set to evoke the time and place of the story. He or she must interact with the lighting, costume, and

(55) makeup designers. Technological advances have led to a **bonanza** of spectacular and **ornate** visual dramas.

A costume designer's work is closely linked to the scene design. Like sets,

(60) costumes must evoke the story's time and place. Costumes may suggest characters' relationships and emotional states.

Finally, the musical director supervises the articulation, phrasing, and dynamics

(65) of each song and chorus. He or she coaches the lead actors, coordinates the ensemble performers, and translates the composer's style and intentions.

1. According to Passage 1, the musical first emerged as an American art form in the
   A) 1920s.
   B) 1930s.
   C) 1940s.
   D) 1950s.

2. As it is used in Passage 1 (line 13), "flaunted" most nearly means
   A) concealed.
   B) revealed.
   C) suggested.
   D) showed off.

3. It can reasonably be inferred from details in Passage 2 that dance routines are now
   A) important in most musicals.
   B) carelessly performed.
   C) rare but intriguing.
   D) too costly to include in musicals.

4. As it is used in Passage 2 (line 39), "qualm" most nearly means
   A) tremor.
   B) embarrassment.
   C) misgiving.
   D) confusion.

5. As it is used in Passage 2 (line 40), "muster" most nearly means
   A) disband.
   B) gather.
   C) dismiss.
   D) duplicate.

6. Which statement best expresses the overall relationship between Passage 1 and Passage 2?
   A) Both passages stress a recent decline in the history of the musical.
   B) Passage 1 investigates the expense of making a musical, while Passage 2 focuses on the history of the genre.
   C) Passage 1 describes the musical's plots while Passage 2 describes the music.
   D) Both passages describe the elements of a complex art form.

7. Passage 2 differs from Passage 1 primarily because it
   A) provides a thorough evaluation of the musical *Oklahoma!*.
   B) focuses exclusively on non-musical elements of productions.
   C) is organized by topic rather than chronologically.
   D) refutes the claim that audiences have come to expect spectacular set designs.

8. Which choice provides the best evidence for the answer to the previous question?
   A) Lines 37–41 ("The financial . . . actors")
   B) Lines 43–44 ("In 1943 . . . milestone")
   C) Lines 53–55 ("He or she . . . designers")
   D) Lines 59–61 ("Like sets . . . and place")

9. How would the author of Passage 1 most likely respond to the list of people crucial to a play's success listed in Passage 2?
   A) The author of Passage 1 would add the music writers and scriptwriters to the list of crucial people.
   B) The author of Passage 1 would not consider the choreographer to be essential to a play's success.
   C) The author of Passage 1 would point out that the audience only cares about what they see on the stage.
   D) The author of Passage 1 would not make any changes to the list provided in Passage 2.

10. As it is used in Passage 2 (line 57), "ornate" most nearly means
    A) stark.
    B) elaborate.
    C) grotesque.
    D) puzzling.

Synonyms

*From the word bank below, choose the word that has the same or nearly the same meaning as the **boldface** word in each sentence and write it on the line. You will not use all of the words.*

aghast	cower	peruse	qualm
annul	deplore	promontory	recourse
assert	instill	proximity	rehabilitate
bask	ornate	pulverize	residue

1. Several people in our apartment complex are working together to **abolish** the restriction on pets. _____

2. This cleaning product promises to get rid of even the most stubborn **remains** of dirt and grease. _____

3. Over time, the forces of erosion will **destroy** solid rock and turn it into sand and dust. _____

4. The performer's **flashy** costume was covered with rhinestones and sequins. _____

5. One way to learn new words is simply to **pore over** a dictionary. _____

6. After a tough season, our team deserved to **revel** in the glory of becoming state champions. _____

7. Without a **second thought,** the movie's villain promised to take control of the city and its resources. _____

8. As the wind picked up, the waves got bigger and crashed harder against the **jetty.** _____

9. Some people **flinch** at the sight of even a small, harmless spider. _____

10. Looking up at the night sky can **infuse** a sense of wonder in just about anyone. _____

11. In a free and open debate, everyone is welcome to **avow** his or her opinion. _____

12. After being fined for overcharging customers, the business is working hard to **rebuild** its image and regain people's trust. _____

Two-Word Completions

Select the pair of words that best completes the meaning of each of the following sentences.

1. During the bloody _____ of the early 1930s, Joseph Stalin "liquidated" every potential rival whom he feared might one day seek to _____ him from his position as absolute master.
   a. repercussions ... sustain
   b. purges ... oust
   c. jurisdictions ... intrigue
   d. premonitions ... ostracize

2. "Using a(n) _____ has caused me a really unexpected problem," the famous novelist remarked. "Most people only know me by my pen name. So if I introduce myself by my real name, I run the risk of being regarded as a complete _____."
   a. addendum ... plebeian
   b. epitaph ... apparition
   c. pseudonym ... nonentity
   d. bolster ... scapegoat

3. Since her objections to the plan were clearly _____, I thought that she was being _____. After all, if she had been serious, her comments would have had more substance.
   a. frivolous ... facetious
   b. inaudible ... forthright
   c. genial ... solicitous
   d. plausible ... articulate

4. Though I tried to _____ my words clearly and distinctly, the roar of the storm caused my voice to be almost _____.
   a. bolster ... abashed
   b. sustain ... ample
   c. muster ... prone
   d. articulate ... inaudible

5. Some of my friends have remarkably _____ memories from which nothing ever seems to escape. Unfortunately, I've been blessed with a memory that is as _____ as a sieve.
   a. retentive ... porous
   b. devoid ... prodigious
   c. staid ... durable
   d. ample ... volatile

6. "His cold and distant attitude toward people clearly betrays his deep _____ for the human race," I observed. "No one who genuinely likes human beings would constantly prefer to remain so _____ from them."
   a. anguish ... prone
   b. obsession ... abashed
   c. apparition ... solicitous
   d. disdain ... aloof

7. Elected officials cannot be too careful about their behavior while in office. If they become _____ about matters of right and wrong, they may do things that the average citizen of this country does not consider _____. Such mistakes could cost the offenders their jobs.
   a. blasé ... ethical
   b. resolute ... indiscriminate
   c. solicitous ... plausible
   d. obsessed ... prodigal

Denotation and Connotation

When you use a dictionary to find a word's definition, you learn the word's denotation, or its literal meaning. A word's **denotation** is its "surface" meaning, and it is generally neutral.

Many words also have connotations. A **connotation** is a word's emotional charge, the meaning that resides "under the surface." Connotations, or implied meanings, build up around words over time. Connotations can be positive or negative. We may associate certain words with positive feelings, yet assign negative meanings to other words that share a similar denotation.

Consider these synonyms for the neutral word *press*.

grind   *crush*   *pulverize*   *demolish*

Grind and *crush* describe less powerful actions than *pulverize* and *demolish*, which are stronger words with more negative connotations.

Look at these examples of words with similar denotations but different connotations.

NEUTRAL	POSITIVE	NEGATIVE
absorbed	**interested**	**obsessed**
instill	**inspire**	**indoctrinate**
sufficient	**ample**	**excessive**

Expressing the Connotation

Read each sentence. Select the word in parentheses that better expresses the connotation (positive, negative, or neutral) given at the beginning of the sentence.

neutral
1. Cassie found out the hard way that other people don't always appreciate her (**biting, facetious**) comments.

positive
2. In Paris, we kept going to the same restaurant to enjoy the wonderful meals that a renowned chef created with remarkable (**skill, finesse**).

neutral
3. The poet, known to be (**solitary, aloof**), spent months on a remote island in the Mediterranean.

positive
4. The con artist was (**blasé, relaxed**) about his role in the heist.

negative
5. The warranty will cover any (**problems, defects**) that appear during the first three months.

neutral
6. Have you ever noticed that most TV butlers are (**staid, snobby**) and seldom talk?

negative
7. After a struggle, the dictator was finally (**dismissed, ousted**) from the palace.

negative
8. Without any warning, the prisoner became irritable and (**volatile, impatient**), demanding to be released.

Classical Roots

cur, curr, curs, cour—
to run

This Latin root appears in **recourse** (page 62). The original meaning was "a running back to," but the word now means "a turning to for help or protection" or "a source of help." Some other words based on the same root are listed below.

concourse	current	incur	recur
courier	discourse	precursor	recurrent

From the list of words above, choose the one that corresponds to each of the brief definitions below. Write the word in the blank space in the illustrative sentence below the definition. Use a dictionary if necessary.

1. a flow, movement; of the present time; in general use
My poem appears in the _____ issue of the school magazine.

2. occurring or appearing repeatedly; returning regularly
Movie soundtracks often use several _____ musical themes.

3. a messenger, usually on urgent or official business
To ensure their safety, the top-secret letters were sent by diplomatic
_____.

4. to happen again, be repeated (*"run again"*)
Disturbing thoughts that _____ frequently may cause a person to seek help from a therapist.

5. a crowd; a thoroughfare; a place where crowds gather (*"running together"*)
We joined the _____ of people in the village square.

6. a forerunner; that which precedes and shows the way
Ancient Athens is considered the _____ of modern democracy.

7. to meet with, run into; to bring upon oneself (*"run into"*)
If you do not stick to a budget, you may _____ unnecessary debts.

8. to talk; a conversation; a long discussion on some topic
The featured speaker delivered a(n) _____ on using the Internet as a research tool.

Read the following passage, taking note of the **boldface** words and their contexts. These words are among those you will be studying in Unit 7. It may help you to complete the exercises in this Unit if you refer to the way the words are used below.

The Discriminating Pigeon
＜Magazine Article＞

by C. W. Senghor

The **attribute** of intelligence is a difficult aspect of animal life to measure. **Predatory** behavior, courtship rituals, nesting instincts, and many other phenomena are relatively easy to describe. But there is no single accepted definition or **doctrine** of intelligence. Nevertheless, scientific experiments have demonstrated sophisticated learning, memory, and problem-solving behavior in a variety of animal species. The chimpanzee remains the **acme** of animal intelligence, with other **exotic** creatures, including dolphins and elephants, not far behind. Less well-known is the remarkable intelligence of the **unassuming** pigeon.

Experiments investigating pigeon intelligence date back 60 years. Few people would list the bird among the world's smartest animals. Some might even **belittle** the pigeon in this regard. But one has to give credit where credit is due. The body of evidence is growing so fast that scientists in the field of animal cognition are practically **wallowing** in data on the mental feats of these familiar birds. The results increasingly **convey** an impression of the pigeon as a curiously discriminating critter.

Experiments dating back to the 1980s indicate that pigeons perform better than most animals on the "mirror test." This test determines whether an animal can recognize its reflection in a mirror. Humans, chimpanzees, and other apes recognize their reflections without prior training, as do elephants and dolphins. Pigeons require training before they associate their reflections with their bodies. Nevertheless, that they can be trained to perform this way makes pigeons unusual. Of course, scientific interpretations of the mirror test have **wavered** over the years. But the study of self-recognition in animals reached a new **juncture** with experiments in which pigeons were alternately shown live and pre-recorded

video images of themselves. The results, published in 2008 by Koji Toda and Shigeru Watanabe, indicate that pigeons can learn to distinguish between live and pre-recorded images of themselves. Self-recognition in pigeons remains a controversial issue. But these experiments support scientists who take a **stance** in favor of the claim that pigeons have a kind of self-awareness.

Professor Watanabe heads the Brain and Evolution unit of Japan's Keio University. Decades of research into animal minds are housed behind his beaming eyes and **jaunty** smile. Among Watanabe's and his colleagues' most intriguing work are experiments in which pigeons were trained to distinguish between paintings by Picasso and paintings by Monet. The trained pigeons could discriminate between paintings by the two artists with remarkable accuracy. In another experiment, pigeons were taught to distinguish between two groups of paintings by children. The first group of paintings had been judged by observers as "good" paintings, while the second group had been

judged as "bad." The pigeons quickly learned the difference and accurately distinguished between "good" and "bad" when shown new paintings.

These experiments are remarkable. But there's little chance that pigeons will replace human art critics in making distinctions between the **tawdry** and the tasteful. The pigeon's ability to discriminate between different kinds of paintings, like its self-recognition, depends on prior training. Left on their own, pigeons don't recognize themselves in mirrors or seem to care much for art. Considerations like these might diminish our awe at the pigeon's mental powers. But there's no chance that the bird's brainy reputation will be entirely **ravaged**. The facts are in, and the pigeons have earned a place in the ranks of our planet's intelligent animals.

Audio

For iWords and audio passages, go to SadlierConnect.com.

Definitions

Note the spelling, pronunciation, part(s) of speech, and definition(s) of each of the following words. Then write the appropriate form of the word in the blank space in the illustrative sentence(s) following.

---

1. attribute
(n., at′ trə byüt;
v., ə trib′ yət)

(n.) a quality or characteristic belonging to or associated with someone or something; (v.) to assign to, credit with; to regard as caused by or resulting from

The _____ I most admire in you is your willingness to give everyone's opinions a fair hearing.

The doctor _____ my runny nose and itchy eyes to multiple allergies.

---

2. convey
(kən vā′)

(v.) to transport; to transmit; to communicate, make known; to transfer ownership or title to

Please _____ our best wishes to your parents on their twenty-fifth wedding anniversary.

---

3. exotic
(ig zät′ ik)

(adj.) foreign; charmingly unfamiliar or strikingly unusual

A recipe may call for _____ herbs and spices that are difficult to obtain.

---

4. haggard
(hag′ ərd)

(adj.) thin, pale, and careworn as a result of worry or suffering; wild-looking

The _____ refugees were given food, clothing, and temporary shelter.

---

5. juncture
(jungk′ chər)

(n.) a joining together; the point at which two things are joined; any important point in time

Our property ends at the _____ of the two stone walls.

---

6. menial
(mē′ nē əl)

(adj.) lowly, humble, lacking importance or dignity; (n.) a person who does the humble and unpleasant tasks

During the Great Depression, people were thankful to have work of any kind, no matter how _____.

Teenagers in need of work can often find jobs as _____ in grocery stores and restaurants.

---

7. parry
(par′ ē)

(v.) to ward off, fend off, evade, avoid; (n.) a defensive movement in fencing and other sports

An effective press secretary can _____ almost any question a reporter asks.

The challenger's swift _____ caught the champion completely off guard.

---

8. tawdry
(tô′ drē)

(*adj.*) showy and flashy but lacking in good taste
An excess of gold braid and glittery beads gave the costumes a _____ look.

9. turncoat
(tərn′ kōt)

(*n.*) a person who switches to an opposing side or party
Strikers generally consider those workers who cross the picket lines to be _____.

10. wallow
(wäl′ ō)

(*v.*) to roll about in a lazy, clumsy, or helpless way; to overindulge in; to have in abundance; (*n.*) a wet, muddy, or dusty area used by animals as a sort of bath; a state of moral or physical collapse
After a strenuous hike, I was too tired to do anything. but _____ blissfully in a hot bath.
On the Serengeti Plain, _____ offer animals much-needed relief from the sun's scorching rays.

Using Context

*For each item, determine whether the **boldface** word from pages 102–103 makes sense in the context of the sentence. Circle the item numbers next to the six sentences in which the words are used correctly.*

1. Although many people dream of vacationing on an **exotic** island or in a faraway land, I am happy to sit under a tree in my backyard and read a book.

2. The officer worked tirelessly to disprove the rumors that he had become a **turncoat**.

3. Surprisingly, the team was able to **wallow** out from behind and achieve a last-minute victory.

4. Unpredictability would not be a good **attribute** in a family pet.

5. We have reached an important **juncture** in our project and must consider our next step.

6. The young violinist won the competition for his melodious and **tawdry** performance.

7. The solitary figure in the opening scene of the movie **conveys** a sense of loneliness.

8. The **haggard** truck is able to travel over all kinds of terrain, including sandy deserts.

9. There is no such thing as a **menial** job on a family farm; every job is important.

10. After each side in the trial presents its case, the jury will meet to **parry** a decision.

Choosing the Right Word

*Select the **boldface** word that better completes each sentence. You might refer to the passage on pages 100–101 to see how most of these words are used in context. Note that the choices might be related forms of the Unit words.*

1. Did you know that some animals (**convey, wallow**) in mud in order to regulate their body temperatures?

2. When I arrived at the critical (**attribute, juncture**) in my career, I realized that my whole future would depend on the decision I was about to make.

3. We were infuriated by the (**haggard, tawdry**) speech in which he tried to portray himself as a great national leader.

4. My mother's dream vacation is to spend several weeks on a(n) (**exotic, menial**) island in the South Pacific.

5. History teaches us that in any great conflict, there will be some (**turncoats, menials**) willing to go over to the enemy.

6. My doctor (**attributed, parried**) my dizziness and vertigo to an inner ear infection.

7. During our trip to China, we sampled such (**tawdry, exotic**) dishes as thousand-year-old eggs and bird's nest soup.

8. After waiting for news of her loved ones for several days, the woman looked careworn and (**haggard, menial**).

9. He is so conceited that it is hard to (**convey, attribute**) to him the simple idea that he did not win the essay competition.

10. So long as you continue to (**parry, wallow**) in self-pity, you will lack the strength needed to solve your problems.

11. No matter how (**menial, tawdry**) the assignment may be, take pride in your work and do your best.

12. Instead of answering my question, the skillful debater (**parried, attributed**) by asking a question of her own.

Completing the Sentence

Choose the word from the word bank that best completes each of the following sentences. Write the correct word or form of the word in the space provided.

attribute	exotic	juncture	parry	turncoat
convey	haggard	menial	tawdry	wallow

1. Two of our divisions were marching rapidly toward each other and hoped to effect a(n) _____ before the enemy attacked.

2. When he switched parties, people called him a(n) _____, but he claimed he'd just had an honest change of opinion.

3. Even though you are starting at a(n) _____ job, you will gain valuable experience and knowledge of how the company works.

4. Since my boss has, as they say, "a short fuse," patience cannot be considered one of her outstanding _____.

5. Most Americans think of Australia as a strange and wonderful continent full of _____ plants and animals.

6. The room was so overcrowded with gaudy furnishings that the overall effect was cheap and _____.

7. Because of his ability to _____ his opponents' blows, he was rarely hurt in his many fights in the ring.

8. We will need several trucks to _____ all the books to the new library building.

9. The drawn and _____ faces of the rescued miners clearly reflected the terrible ordeal they had survived.

10. During our safari trip in Kenya, we took many pictures of hippos as they _____ in a mudhole.

Definitions

Note the spelling, pronunciation, part(s) of speech, and definition(s) of each of the following words. Then write the appropriate form of the word in the blank space in the illustrative sentence(s) following.

1. acme
(ak′ mē)

(*n.*) the highest point
A perfect game is the _____ of any pitcher's career in baseball.

2. belittle
(bi lit′ əl)

(*v.*) to make something appear smaller than it is; to refer to in a way that suggests lack of importance or value
Candidates for public office may resort to negative ads that _____ their opponents' records.

3. doctrine
(däk′ trin)

(*n.*) a belief, principle, or teaching; a system of such beliefs or principles; a formulation of such beliefs or principles
No two religions see eye to eye on every fine detail of _____.

4. excise
(*v.*, ek sīz′;
n., ek′ sīz)

(*v.*) to remove by cutting; (*n.*) an indirect tax on the manufacture, sale, or distribution of a commodity or service
If you _____ that irrelevant remark, you will improve your essay.
The _____ imposed on products such as tobacco and alcohol have skyrocketed.

5. jaunty
(jôn′ tē)

(*adj.*) lively, easy, and carefree in manner; smart or trim in appearance
I bought a _____ straw hat.

6. predatory
(pred′ ə tôr ē)

(*adj.*) preying on, plundering, or piratical
Owls and other _____ birds play an important role in maintaining the balance of nature.

7. ravage
(rav′ ij)

(*v.*) to destroy, lay waste, ruin; (*n.*) ruinous damage, destruction
Swarms of locusts _____ the farmer's fields and orchards.
No one can escape the _____ of time.

8. stance
(stans)

(*n.*) a way of holding the body; an attitude or position on an issue
A fashion model's _____ is calculated to show off a designer's clothing to best advantage.

9. **unassuming**
(ən ə sü′ miŋ)

(*adj.*) not putting on airs, unpretentious; modest

Many celebrities remain _____
despite their fame and wealth.

10. **waver**
(wā′ vər)

(*v.*) to move to and fro, become unsteady; to show lack of firmness or decision

The committee _____ for several
days before choosing the winner of the essay contest.

Using Context

*For each item, determine whether the **boldface** word from pages 106–107 makes sense in the context of the sentence. Circle the item numbers next to the six sentences in which the words are used correctly.*

1. The pickpocket lurks outside the bank in his **predatory** manner, waiting to snatch the full wallets of unsuspecting pedestrians.

2. My speech teacher suggested that I **excise** any unnecessary pieces of information so that I would not appear to be going off topic.

3. The **jaunty** expression on my friend's face told me that he did not get the lead role in the play as he hoped he would.

4. I was grateful that rather than **belittle** my goal of one day becoming a famous author, my teacher gave me advice on how to start a path to that career.

5. My younger sister was thrilled when I allowed her to **ravage** my toy collection, as she now has twice as many toys to play with.

6. When I was trying to decide whether to join the basketball or track team, my mother warned me not to **waver** so long that I missed both tryouts.

7. Her personal **doctrine** that no one is more or less important than anyone else means that she treats everyone with the equal amount of kindness and respect.

8. She is an unfriendly person, so I fear that her **unassuming** nature means that she will be taken advantage of by deceitful people.

9. His **stance** as he stood in the corner, with crossed arms and eyes looking down, suggested that he did not want anyone to talk to him.

10. I thought that getting splashed with water from a passing bus was the **acme** of my morning, only to find that things would get worse as the day went on.

Choosing the Right Word

*Select the **boldface** word that better completes each sentence. You might refer to the passage on pages 100–101 to see how most of these words are used in context. Note that the choices might be related forms of the Unit words.*

1. For many years the towns and villages along the Normandy coast of France showed the (**ravages, doctrines**) of the great invasion of 1944.

2. Americans expect candidates to take a definite (**stance, acme**) on each of the important issues in a national election.

3. When asked about your commitment to your values, do not (**waver, belittle**) but stand firm in your beliefs.

4. He hoped that election to the presidency would be the (**acme, doctrine**) of his long and brilliant career in public service.

5. Even after pitching two no-hit games this season, Stan was the same quiet and (**jaunty, unassuming**) boy we had always known.

6. One must be careful these days, as (**unassuming, predatory**) phone calls from dishonest companies are on the rise.

7. "If we are to keep the body politic healthy," the senator remarked, "we must (**excise, waver**) the cancer of racial prejudice from it."

8. The captain was deeply worried, even though he tried hard to appear confident and (**predatory, jaunty**) to the passengers.

9. Our system of justice is based on the (**acme, doctrine**) that defendants are presumed innocent unless the prosecution can prove them guilty.

10. The immigrants never (**excised, wavered**) in their determination to become American citizens.

11. I am thoroughly disgusted by people who try to make themselves seem more important than they really are by (**belittling, ravaging**) others.

12. Thieves are essentially a (**predatory, jaunty**) class of criminals because they live off what they can take from others.

Completing the Sentence

Choose the word from the word bank that best completes each of the following sentences. Write the correct word or form of the word in the space provided.

acme	doctrine	jaunty	ravage	unassuming
belittle	excise	predatory	stance	waver

1. In the early nineteenth century, Thomas Bowdler attempted to "clean up" the works of Shakespeare by _exercise_ all words and phrases that he felt were coarse or offensive.

2. The author's first published work was a(n) _unassuming_ little pamphlet on the joys of fly fishing.

3. In her most celebrated novels, such as *Pride and Prejudice* and *Emma*, Jane Austen reached the _acme_ of her literary art.

4. I agree that we should not exaggerate her achievements, but we should not _belittle_ them either.

5. The Monroe _doctrine_ sought to prevent the colonization of the American continents by European powers.

6. She sat there staring at the menu, _wavering_ between the steak sandwich and the chef's salad.

7. Though many _predatory_ creatures prefer to hunt at night, lions and leopards are active during the daytime.

8. Disease had so _ravaged_ his once-handsome face that I scarcely recognized him!

9. Her happy expression and the _jaunty_ way she walked down the street gave the impression of someone "on top of the world."

10. A baseball player who improves his _stance_ at the plate usually improves his batting average, too.

Synonyms

*Choose the word or form of the word from this Unit that is the same or most nearly the same in meaning as the **boldface** word or expression in the phrase. Write that word on the line. Use a dictionary if necessary.*

1. at the **peak** of her career   _____
2. sought to **deflect** the force of the assault   _____
3. seldom **falters** under pressure   _____
4. the **policy** of equal justice for all   _____
5. embodies the **traits** of a leader   _____
6. at a critical **turning point** in the relationship   _____
7. **carried** the trash to the dumpster   _____
8. the **exploitative** behavior of big banks   _____
9. lived in **unpretentious** homes despite their wealth   _____
10. **bask in** the mud to keep cool   _____
11. **minimized** his achievements   _____
12. had an unpopular **point of view**   _____
13. **demolished** by a series of storms   _____
14. a closet filled with **garish** outfits   _____
15. will **delete** the paragraph from the contract   _____

Antonyms

*Choose the word or form of the word from this Unit that is most nearly opposite in meaning to the **boldface** word or expression in the phrase. Write that word on the line. Use a dictionary if necessary.*

1. became a **loyalist** after the rally   _____
2. a **radiant** expression on her face   _____
3. a **mournful** musical score   _____
4. preferred more **familiar** foods   _____
5. undertaking a **grand** endeavor   _____

Writing: Words in Action

Suppose Professor Watanabe has asked you to write an article for a local newspaper to persuade readers that pigeons are not public nuisances. Summarize Dr. Watanabe's findings, and make a strong case for the intelligence of the pigeon. Use details from the passage (pages 100–101) and three or more words from this Unit.

Vocabulary in Context

*Some of the words you have studied in this Unit appear in **boldface** type. Read the passage below, and then circle the letter of the correct answer for each word as it is used in context.*

Willy the chicken was a well-known figure around New York City's Chinatown and attracted thousands of tourists to the little amusement arcade on Mott Street where he held court. His owners would **parry** any charge that he was ever ill-treated. Willy was not one of those **haggard** city chickens we still see pecking among the traffic, nor did he perform **menial** duties as a neighborhood alarm clock. He was never a **turncoat** to his proud species. Willy was a star—and he showed every sign of loving it.

Willy played tic-tac-toe with anyone who put 50 cents in the slot at the front of his cage. Being a chicken, none of his human challengers minded much when Willy went first. The remarkable thing about Willy, however, was not just that he could play tic-tac-toe—though that was a rare enough accomplishment among chickens—but that he never lost. He **excised** all opposition with surgical precision.

He used to stand in a glass cage with a lit-up tic-tac-toe screen at the back. When it flashed "Your Turn," the challenger would push a button to place an X on the screen. When it flashed "Bird's Turn," Willy would go behind an opaque pane of glass marked "Thinkin' Booth." When he had thought, he would peck once to place his O. Then he would come out, stare beadily at his opponent, and win.

Willy died on July 28, 1993. Playing tic-tac-toe with Willy was the **acme** of arcade fun for many.

---

1. What is the meaning of **parry** as it is used in paragraph 1?
   a. ignore
   b. admit
   c. fend off
   d. deny

2. In paragraph 1, what does the use of the word **haggard** suggest about city chickens?
   a. They are very old.
   b. They are worried and thin.
   c. They crow at dawn.
   d. They do not live long.

3. The word **menial** means about the same as
   a. humble
   b. hardworking
   c. antisocial
   d. criminal

4. Which word means the same as **turncoat** as it is used in paragraph 1?
   a. loyalist
   b. opportunist
   c. fair-weather friend
   d. traitor

5. What does **excised** most likely mean as it is used in paragraph 2?
   a. cut out
   b. triumphed over
   c. won against
   d. wiped out

6. **Acme** comes from the Greek word **akme. Akme** most likely means
   a. achiever
   b. winner
   c. highest point
   d. benchmark

Read the following passage, taking note of the **boldface** words and their contexts. These words are among those you will be studying in Unit 8. It may help you to complete the exercises in this Unit if you refer to the way the words are used below.

Aquatic Robotics
<Technical Essay>

Two-thirds of Earth's surface is covered with water. Human beings have yet to **infiltrate** most of this unexplored and **cryptic** terrain. Instead, their most important **proxies** underwater are robots. The field of undersea robotics has grown rapidly in recent years. It is now an essential part of ocean exploration.

At the very foundation of robot design is the performance of tasks that are difficult, repetitive, or dangerous. These same words describe undersea exploration. For example, the important missions of marine research often require a descent to great depths. Vast areas of the ocean floor remain inaccessible to humans no matter what protective **attire** they wear or equipment they use. And no eager explorer, however **fervent**, would carry out a deep diving **stint** lasting months at a time. Robotics engineers began to pick up on these challenges in the 1990s. They channeled their efforts into developing three **divergent** types of undersea robots. One type is a remote-controlled vehicle that is towed behind ships. Another type is really a miniature submarine that carries a human crew and is equipped with robot arms. A third type of robot is fully autonomous, carrying out a survey in an **unflagging** fashion that no human could hope to match.

Undersea robots are designed to aid humans in a variety of endeavors. Some of these are

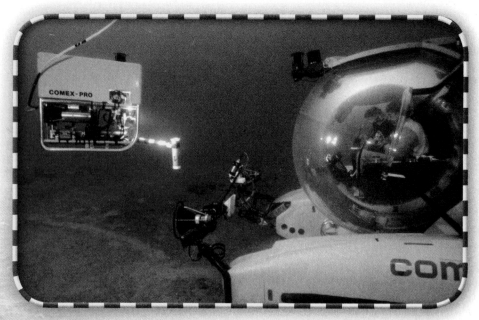

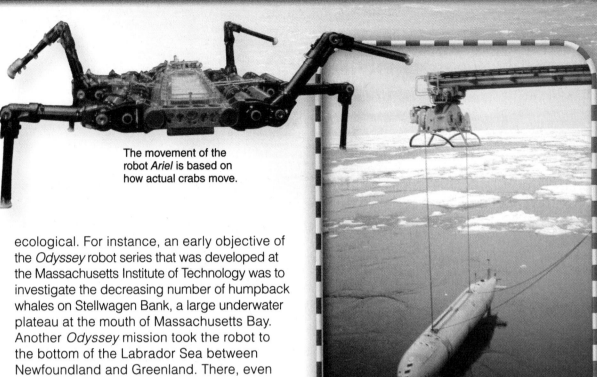

The movement of the robot *Ariel* is based on how actual crabs move.

ecological. For instance, an early objective of the *Odyssey* robot series that was developed at the Massachusetts Institute of Technology was to investigate the decreasing number of humpback whales on Stellwagen Bank, a large underwater plateau at the mouth of Massachusetts Bay. Another *Odyssey* mission took the robot to the bottom of the Labrador Sea between Newfoundland and Greenland. There, even the notoriously rough winter weather could not **nullify** the robot's mission to explore ocean oxygenation. In this process, surface waters in high latitudes near the poles become oxygen-rich but also cold and dense. The cold, dense water **plummets** to the bottom in plumes, where it provides energy for many kinds of life. Without *Odyssey's* assistance in such missions, human efforts would have been to no **avail**, given the conditions. The latest *Odyssey* robot can even hover in place, like a helicopter. It can be controlled remotely with a joystick.

Scientists are not the only ones using aquatic robots. Undersea robots are also important for military uses. The robot crab *Ariel*, for example, may be used to clear mines from minefields that **abut** the shore. No obstacle or crevice stops *Ariel*. Few humans would remain calm and **stoical** performing such a hazardous duty. Military robots are also used to find enemy submarines and to protect coastal areas.

At present, there is virtually no **perceptible** limit on the array of uses for undersea robotics. The British independent robot *Autosub4*, for example, has been used to explore herring behavior in the North Sea and to locate valuable metals at the bottom of a Scottish lake. Tethered underwater vehicles called ROVs have assisted marine archaeologists in locating and exploring shipwrecks, including that of the *Titanic*. And after the massive Gulf oil spill disaster in 2010, cleanup analyses and efforts relied heavily on ROVs. It is safe to **proclaim** that undersea exploration in the twenty-first century will increasingly be the domain of robots as they go where humans cannot hope to follow.

Audio

For iWords and audio passages, go to SadlierConnect.com.

Definitions

Note the spelling, pronunciation, part(s) of speech, and definition(s) of each of the following words. Then write the appropriate form of the word in the blank space in the illustrative sentence(s) following.

1. abut
(ə bət')

(*v.*) to join at one end or be next to; to support, prop up

Land that _____ a river or lake is considered a highly desirable location on which to build a summer home.

2. attire
(ə tīr')

(*n.*) clothes, apparel, garb; (*v.*) to dress, adorn, or bedeck

The special _____ that firefighters wear helps to protect them from flames and smoke.

The children happily _____ their stuffed animals in holiday outfits and accessories.

3. crony
(krō' nē)

(*n.*) a very close friend, chum, buddy

We have been _____ ever since we met in the second grade.

4. divergent
(də vər' jənt)

(*adj.*) going in different directions; different from each other; departing from convention, deviant

Two people may be close friends despite their having very _____ interests and beliefs.

5. gaunt
(gônt)

(*adj.*) thin and bony, starved looking; bare, barren

We left food and water for the _____ alley cat.

6. nullify
(nəl' ə fī)

(*v.*) to make of no value or consequence, cancel, wipe out

After seven days, you cannot _____ the contract without being charged a penalty.

7. plummet
(pləm' ət)

(*v.*) to plunge straight down; (*n.*) a weight fastened to a line

Gannets and other seabirds _____ headfirst into the ocean to catch small fish and squid.

Experts think the pierced round stones found at the site served as _____ to weight fishing nets.

8. rankle
(raŋ' kəl)

(*v.*) to cause anger, irritation, or bitterness (with the suggestion that the pain grows worse with time)

Insults may _____ a person for many years.

9. **scavenger**
(skav′ ən jər)

(*n.*) a person who collects or removes usable items from waste materials; an animal that feeds on refuse or dead bodies

A few _____ such as catfish and other bottom feeders will help to keep a fish tank clean.

10. **stoical**
(stō′ i kəl)

(*adj.*) self-controlled, not showing feeling in response to pleasure or pain

The refugees' _____ acceptance of their plight was deeply moving.

Using Context

*For each item, determine whether the **boldface** word from pages 114–115 makes sense in the context of the sentence. Circle the item numbers next to the six sentences in which the words are used correctly.*

1. Members of both teams sent the injured player their most **divergent** wishes for a speedy recovery.

2. In the desert, very warm daytime temperatures can **plummet** to very cold nighttime lows.

3. We plan to visit vintage clothing stores to find the proper **attire** for our 1980s-themed dance party.

4. The military officers were careful not to reveal the latest battle plans because they suspected that there was a **crony** among them.

5. According to scientists, *Tyrannosaurus rex* was both a fierce hunter and a keen **scavenger**.

6. The oral surgeon complimented me on my ability to remain calm and **stoical** as my tooth was extracted.

7. When the archaeologists finish excavating the layers of sand and rock that cover the ancient city, these fascinating ancient ruins will finally **abut**.

8. In an attempt to **nullify** the jury's verdict in her client's first trial, the defense attorney argued that her predecessor had been unqualified and incompetent.

9. The song's bright, witty lyrics **rankle** perfectly with its catchy melody.

10. The black-and-white photos of the **gaunt** prisoners of war moved us deeply.

Choosing the Right Word

*Select the **boldface** word that better completes each sentence. You might refer to the passage on pages 112–113 to see how most of these words are used in context. Note that the choices might be related forms of the Unit words.*

1. President Kennedy bore his pain in such a (**divergent, stoical**) manner that few people realized how much he suffered from his World War II back injury.

2. Our farm used to (**rankle, abut**) the high school football field, but now a highway separates the two tracts of land.

3. I pretended that being ignored by the "best people in town" meant nothing to me, but actually those snubs (**rankled, nullified**) deeply.

4. The (**stoical, gaunt**) and leafless trees seemed to add to the gloom of that wintry scene.

5. It is a sad fact of experience that postwar political blunders can often (**nullify, plummet**) or even reverse the results of battlefield triumphs.

6. If we had a good civil service system in this town, the mayor wouldn't be able to put his (**cronies, scavengers**) on the public payroll.

7. After the big snowstorm, the trees seemed to be (**attired, cronies**) in white lace.

8. Our hopes for a winning touchdown (**nullified, plummeted**) in the last minute when Jim fumbled and South High recovered the ball.

9. I understand that pigeons are (**plummets, scavengers**) by nature, but I still don't like them pecking around our picnic table, looking for crumbs.

10. When the temperature suddenly (**plummeted, nullified**) to below freezing, the hikers made the wise decision to descend the mountain.

11. Although the woman was filled with grief, she remained (**gaunt, stoical**) during the poignant memorial service.

12. In a democracy, we expect people to have (**gaunt, divergent**) views and to express them openly.

Completing the Sentence

Choose the word from the word bank that best completes each of the following sentences. Write the correct word or form of the word in the space provided.

abut	crony	gaunt	plummet	scavenger
attire	divergent	nullify	rankle	stoical

1. We decided not to buy the house, mainly because the property it sits on unfortunately __abut__ the noisy main highway.

2. To prepare for the job interview, she _____ herself in a simple but elegant navy-blue suit.

3. The rise in the cost of living _____ my efforts to save some money from my small salary.

4. We watched in dismay as our new model airplane suddenly went out of control and __plummeted__ to the ground.

5. His failure to win the election _____ in his mind until it caused a complete emotional breakdown.

6. The witnesses' statements are so _____ that it's hard to know how the accident actually happened.

7. He tried to appear _____ when he heard the bad news, but I realized that he was deeply hurt.

8. Shakespeare said that Cassius had a "lean and hungry look," but I would describe him with the single word _____.

9. My father has three _____ who go with him each year on a camping trip in the High Sierras.

10. Although the vulture has a decidedly poor reputation, it does a useful job as a(n) _____, clearing away decaying matter.

Definitions

Note the spelling, pronunciation, part(s) of speech, and definition(s) of each of the following words. Then write the appropriate form of the word in the blank space in the illustrative sentence(s) following.

1. avail
(ə vāl′)

(*v.*) to be of use or benefit to; to make use of; to take advantage of; to profit or benefit; (*n.*) use, benefit, or value

Be sure to _____ yourself of all the services that the school library has to offer.

I tried repeatedly to contact my neighbor by phone, but to absolutely no _____.

2. cryptic
(krip′ tik)

(*adj.*) puzzling, mystifying, or enigmatic

The letter to the editor was so _____ that I couldn't be certain what the writer had actually intended to say.

3. enmity
(en′ mə tē)

(*n.*) hatred, ill-will

Despite a long, close, and tense match, the defeated player felt no _____ toward the new champion.

4. fervent
(fər′ vənt)

(*adj.*) very earnest, emotional, passionate; extremely hot

The President delivered a _____ plea for tolerance and unity.

5. infiltrate
(in′ fil trāt)

(*v.*) to pass through or gain entrance to gradually or stealthily

Some of our men _____ the enemy's camp and captured their leader.

6. perceptible
(pər sep′ tə bəl)

(*adj.*) capable of being grasped by the senses or mind

There was no _____ improvement in the patient's condition despite the doctors' best efforts to treat the infection.

7. proclaim
(prō klām′)

(*v.*) to declare publicly or officially

We _____ loyalty to our country when we recite the Pledge of Allegiance.

8. proxy
(präk′ sē)

(*n.*) an agent, substitute; a written permission allowing one person to act in another's place

The Vice President may be called upon to be the President's _____ at the funeral of a foreign leader.

9. stint
(stint)

(*v.*) to limit, be sparing or frugal; (*n.*) a limit or restriction; a fixed share of work or duty; a period of activity

Good hosts never _____ on food and drink for the guests who attend their parties.

A _____ as the guest host of a popular talk show may be a big career break for a young comedian.

10. unflagging
(ən flag′ iŋ)

(*adj.*) tireless, continuing with vigor

After the votes were counted, the candidates paid tribute to the _____ loyalty of their supporters.

Using Context

*For each item, determine whether the **boldface** word from pages 118–119 makes sense in the context of the sentence. Circle the item numbers next to the six sentences in which the words are used correctly.*

1. Although my **stint** as a waiter wasn't what I wanted to do in the long term, it gave me valuable experience in dealing with difficult people.

2. I was delighted when he finished my favorite book and reacted simply with **enmity**.

3. After hours of attempting to fix the leak, he turned the water back on and saw that his efforts were of little **avail**.

4. The environmental club decided to **infiltrate** their message about going green by putting posters in every classroom and hallway throughout the school.

5. After leaving a few polite notes asking her upstairs neighbors to be quiet, she left a **cryptic** voicemail explaining that she would call the police if the noise continued.

6. Tom becomes interested in causes but is so **unflagging** that he moves from one to another.

7. The executive named a colleague who could act as her **proxy** since she would not be able to attend the next board meeting.

8. The teacher was not only furious that the student strolled into the classroom half an hour late, but also that he did so with no **perceptible** sense of guilt.

9. I will **proclaim** my intention to run for student council at the next assembly.

10. The spokesperson's **fervent** speech about the importance of the charitable organization clearly resonated with many people, as donations tripled in the following hour.

Choosing the Right Word

*Select the **boldface** word that better completes each sentence. You might refer to the passage on pages 112–113 to see how most of these words are used in context. Note that the choices might be related forms of the Unit words.*

1. In the unforgettable words of the Declaration of Independence, Jefferson (**proclaimed, infiltrated**) to the world that a new nation had been born.

2. Let me state my absolute (**proxy, enmity**) for those who seek to bring about political change through violent means.

3. In spite of my efforts to keep them at bay, spring weeds always manage to (**infiltrate, proclaim**) my vegetable garden.

4. The moon is sometimes faintly (**cryptic, perceptible**) in the morning sky.

5. All the heroism of our men could not (**proclaim, avail**) against the enemy's superior forces.

6. Large numbers of stockholders allowed (**stints, proxies**) to vote in their place.

7. It didn't take me long to master the (**fervent, cryptic**) greetings, signs, and handshakes that were part of the club's rituals.

8. The two candidates are working hard to get the voters' support, but in my opinion there is no (**perceptible, cryptic**) difference between them.

9. Before going to college, my brother did a (**stint, proxy**) as an apprentice radio operator on an oceangoing tanker.

10. During the prolonged dry spell, the farmers' (**fervent, perceptible**) prayers for rain were seldom answered.

11. For her (**unflagging, cryptic**) devotion to every good cause in our community, we honor this wonderful woman.

12. We made phone calls, sent emails, and combed the neighborhood on foot, but our search for the lost dog was to no (**stint, avail**).

Completing the Sentence

Choose the word from the word bank that best completes each of the following sentences. Write the correct word or form of the word in the space provided.

avail	enmity	infiltrate	proclaim	stint
cryptic	fervent	perceptible	proxy	unflagging

1. Instead of giving us a clear and helpful answer, the speaker offered only the _cryptic_ prophecy that "time will tell."

2. All her efforts to get more business for her troubled company proved to be of no _avail_, and the store had to close down.

3. Each year the President _proclaims_ the last Thursday in November as a day of national thanksgiving.

4. Since I will not be able to attend the meeting, I hereby appoint Ms. Brown to act as my _Proxy_.

5. Over a period of years, words and phrases used in the field of computer science _infultrate_ everyday speech.

6. Even after he retired and we expected him to slow down, his efforts in support of his beloved school remained _____.

7. As a teenager, she developed a(n) _fervent_ interest in biology that led to a lifelong career.

8. In our community, people of many ethnic backgrounds work together without jealousy or _enmity_.

9. Their parents had _stint_ for many years to save the money needed to send the children to college.

10. I didn't think she would have the nerve to ask me for a loan, but she did—and with no _perceptible_ embarrassment.

Synonyms

*Choose the word or form of the word from this Unit that is the same or most nearly the same in meaning as the **boldface** word or expression in the phrase. Write that word on the line. Use a dictionary if necessary.*

1. lingering **antagonism** despite the settlement _____
2. plan to visit an old **pal** _____
3. as **scrawny** as a skeleton _____
4. forced to **cut back** even on necessities _____
5. property that **borders** a nature preserve _____
6. a **forager** in search of food _____
7. a barely **noticeable** scar _____
8. **penetrate** the intelligence agency _____
9. temperatures **fell suddenly** _____
10. **unremitting** interest in celebrity gossip _____
11. selected to act as my **representative** _____
12. will not **benefit** if not properly done _____
13. **broadcast** my intention to run for office _____
14. packed **outfits** suitable for all kinds of weather _____
15. an **ardent** advocate for the poor _____

Antonyms

*Choose the word or form of the word from this Unit that is most nearly opposite in meaning to the **boldface** word or expression in the phrase. Write that word on the line. Use a dictionary if necessary.*

1. trying to **delight** the audience _____
2. able to follow the **crystal clear** message _____
3. **endorse** the captain's order _____
4. had an **emotional** response to the proposal _____
5. someone with **orthodox** views _____

Writing: Words in Action

How do you think aquatic robots and deep-sea exploration will change our lives? Will they lead to improvements? If so, what benefits might they yield? Write a newspaper editorial expressing your views on the potential of aquatic robots. Use details from the passage (pages 112–113) and three or more words from this Unit.

Vocabulary in Context

*Some of the words you have studied in this Unit appear in **boldface** type. Read the passage below, and then circle the letter of the correct answer for each word as it is used in context.*

The word *robot* was invented by Czech playwright, novelist, and journalist Karel Čapek (1880–1938). He introduced the word to the world in his play *R.U.R.*, or *Rossum's Universal Robots*, which was first produced in Prague in 1920. The idea of artificial life goes all the way back to antiquity, but Čapek was a brilliant and **unflagging scavenger** of ideas and language, and he created a work of great originality and enormous influence.

The word *robot* comes from the word *rabota*, which belongs to an ancient language of worship known as "Church Slavonic." This beautiful, **gaunt** language dates back to the ninth century and is still used by the Orthodox Church in the Czech Republic and several other Eastern European countries. *Rabota* is a medieval word for the duty of forced labor that serfs owed to the lord whose land they lived on.

Čapek's play takes place in a factory—R.U.R.—that makes machines that resemble humans. These humanoid robots are created to save humans the trouble of doing any work. R.U.R. uses the latest biology, chemistry, and electronics to mass-produce workers who think, talk, move, and learn just like humans. They lack nothing but a soul and the ability to love. In time, however, they learn to feel both love and **enmity**. Servitude begins to **rankle**, and they revolt against the factory bosses and their **cronies**, and then all their human overlords.

Does the plot of *R.U.R* look familiar? Modern science fiction clearly owes Čapek much more than just a single word.

---

1. What is the meaning of **unflagging** as it is used in paragraph 1?
   a. listless   **c.** tireless
   b. shameless   **d.** fearless

2. In paragraph 1, what does the use of the word **scavenger** suggest about Čapek?
   a. He was unoriginal.   **c.** He was a thief.
   b. He collected   **d.** He was
   ideas.   wide-ranging.

3. The word **gaunt** means about the same as
   a. expressive   **c.** incomprehensible
   b. rich   **d.** lean

4. **Enmity** comes from the Latin word **inimicus. Inimicus** most likely means
   a. affection   **c.** enemy
   b. loyalty   **d.** friend

5. Which word means the same as **rankle** as it is used in paragraph 3?
   a. irritate   **c.** accumulate
   b. survive   **d.** intensify

6. What does **cronies** most likely mean as it is used in paragraph 3?
   a. co-workers   **c.** employees
   b. superiors   **d.** buddies

Read the following passage, taking note of the **boldface** words and their contexts. These words are among those you will be studying in Unit 9. It may help you to complete the exercises in this Unit if you refer to the way the words are used below.

Tecumseh of the Shawnee
<Biographical Sketch>

Tecumseh

The great Shawnee leader, Tecumseh (Shooting Star), was born in 1768 in Ohio country. Like the land he was born to, the 45 years of his life were marked by war. Control of the fertile region had been contested for centuries, even before Europeans arrived. By the time Tecumseh was born, the British were the region's dominant power. British settlement continued to expand westward, **encroaching** on tribal lands. Irritated tribal leaders **chafed** at the expansion, and some sought to **fend** off the tide of settlers with violence. One of these leaders was Tecumseh's father, who was killed in a battle with the British in 1774. Soon after, the Shawnee sided with the British against the American colonies in the Revolutionary War.

When the Revolutionary War ended in 1783, Tecumseh was 15 years old. American forces continued to clash with tribes in Ohio and the surrounding region in a prolonged conflict referred to as the Northwest Indian War. Tecumseh fought in many battles and became the leader of a band of Shawnee warriors. The Northwest Indian War ended in 1794, with the Native Americans forced to **capitulate** and hand over most of the Ohio lands to the United States. Tensions between the native tribes and settlers cooled. Many tribal leaders even encouraged their people to adopt aspects of the settlers' culture.

This period of relative calm did not last long. Many Native Americans remained **disgruntled** at the spread of settlements and the now **predominant** U.S. authority that allowed settlers to take land with **impunity**. A true warrior never seeks glory, but by 1808, Tecumseh had emerged as a leader of **renown**. He travelled throughout the region to build an alliance strong enough to confront the United States. In his new role as a political leader, Tecumseh was a **prodigy**. He was a talented and **disarming** speaker, full of

William Henry Harrison c. 1812

poise and purpose. **Endowed** with an impressive physique, he presented a charismatic **mien**. He won thousands over to his cause. Tecumseh's Confederacy, as it came to be known, drew together many tribes.

The situation grew **dire** with the signing of the Treaty of Fort Wayne, which opened some three million acres of land to U.S. settlers. Tecumseh and 400 warriors met with Governor William Henry Harrison of the Indiana Territory to demand the treaty be nullified. When Harrison refused, Tecumseh headed south to recruit more allies for his Confederacy. Tribal forces carried out scattered raids on white settlers. While Tecumseh was away, Harrison led about 1000 militia and army troops to Prophetstown. There he defeated the main force of Tecumseh's Confederacy at the Battle of Tippecanoe on November 7, 1811. Memory of that victory would serve Harrison well decades later as he sought to become the ninth president. Tecumseh, on the other hand, saw his plans begin to go **awry**. The Confederacy, **bludgeoned** by the defeat, would now take more time to develop.

As Tecumseh set out to rebuild the Confederacy, the War of 1812 broke out between Britain and the United States. The conflicts in the Northwest were one of the leading causes of this war, as many in the United States blamed the British for inciting the Native Americans to violence and supplying them with firearms. Tecumseh sided with the British and helped them defeat the Americans at Detroit. About a year later, Tecumseh was killed during the Battle of the Thames on October 5, 1813. His Confederacy surrendered soon after, giving the United States control over the Northwest frontier.

Audio

For iWords and audio passages, go to SadlierConnect.com.

Definitions

Note the spelling, pronunciation, part(s) of speech, and definition(s) of each of the following words. Then write the appropriate form of the word in the blank space in the illustrative sentence(s) following.

1. awry
(ə rī′)

(*adj., adv.*) in a turned or twisted position or direction; wrong, out of the right or hoped-for course

After running to catch the bus, I realized that my clothing was all _____.

If something went _____ during a countdown, NASA officials would cancel a shuttle launch.

2. bludgeon
(bləj′ ən)

(*n.*) a short club used as a weapon; (*v.*) to strike with a heavy club; to use force or strong arguments to gain some point

Early humans fashioned _____ from the thick limbs of trees.

Heavy-handed writers tend to _____ readers with explanations of their characters' motives.

3. chafe
(chāf)

(*v.*) to warm by rubbing; to wear sore by rubbing; to feel annoyance or dissatisfaction, annoy, irk; to strain or press against; (*n.*) a sore or injury caused by rubbing

The American colonists _____ under the many unjust laws imposed on them by King George III.

To keep that raw _____ from becoming infected, you should put a clean bandage on it.

4. dire
(dīr)

(*adj.*) dreadful, causing fear or suffering; warning of trouble to come; demanding immediate action to avoid disaster

Environmentalists warn of the _____ consequences of the destruction of the world's rain forests.

5. encroach
(en krōch′)

(*v.*) to advance beyond the usual or proper limits, trespass

Where suburbs _____ on unspoiled forests or wetlands, delicate ecosystems may be disrupted.

6. fend
(fend)

(*v.*) to ward off, resist; to get along, manage

The picnic was enjoyable, but we spent quite a bit of time _____ off ants and mosquitos.

7. mien
(mēn)

(*n.*) air, manner; appearance; expression

A person may adopt a cheerful _____ in an attempt to conceal sorrow or anger.

8. **penal**
(pē′ nəl)

(*adj.*) having to do with punishment
Devil's Island, off the coast of French Guiana, was once the site of an infamous _____ colony.

9. **predominant**
(pri däm′ ə nənt)

(*adj.*) the greatest in strength or power; most common
Cy Young, for whom the coveted pitching award is named, was once the _____ pitcher in baseball.

10. **recluse**
(re′ klüs)

(*n.*) a person who leads a life shut up or withdrawn from the world
An individual who has suffered a great emotional loss may become something of a _____.

Using Context

For each item, determine whether the **boldface** word from pages 126–127 makes sense in the context of the sentence. Circle the item numbers next to the six sentences in which the words are used correctly.

1. The stranded hikers feared that their situation would become **dire** if rescuers did not find them by nightfall.

2. Historical evidence suggests that they were a nonviolent, peaceful society known to solve disputes using the tools of negotiation, compromise, and **bludgeon**.

3. The repetitive action of rowing may **chafe** the skin on your hands if you do it often.

4. The beach was so crowded that it was hard to set up a chair and an umbrella and not **encroach** on someone else's space.

5. Paleontologists study dinosaur fossils and other physical traces of **predominant** times.

6. Pets are dependent on humans and cannot be expected to **fend** for themselves.

7. In a debate, it is not enough to simply state your **mien**; you must also support it.

8. As a former criminal court judge, this candidate for governor can truly claim to be an expert on our state **penal** code.

9. A burrow is a safe **recluse** in which an animal can store food and hide from enemies.

10. It was the kind of day when anything that could possibly go **awry** did, so I decided to go home and lay low before something really terrible happened.

Choosing the Right Word

Select the **boldface** word that better completes each sentence. You might refer to the passage on pages 124–125 to see how most of these words are used in context. Note that the choices might be related forms of the Unit words.

1. Do you understand how someone can live as a (**mien, recluse**) even in the midst of a great city?

2. Why does she (**bludgeon, fend**) people she barely knows with her arguments and strong opinions?

3. The lecturer is a man who served ten years in prison and is now devoting his life to bringing about reforms in our (**penal, predominant**) system.

4. As we use up the earth's fossil-fuel supplies, we are faced with an increasingly (**penal, dire**) need to develop new energy sources.

5. Mosses and lichens—which can survive extremely cold temperatures—are (**predominant, dire**) plants in the Arctic tundra.

6. Yes, we are still friends, but not as close as we used to be; something has gone (**awry, dire**) in our relationship.

7. His plain clothing and quiet (**bludgeon, mien**) were not what we expected in a famous Hollywood director.

8. During the winter the wind usually blows from the north in that area, but during the summer southerly currents are (**predominant, awry**).

9. My problem was to (**fend, bludgeon**) off their unwelcome attentions without being openly insulting.

10. The rights guaranteed by the U.S. Constitution do not permit citizens to (**fend, encroach**) on the rights of others.

11. After a horrible accident, the one-time celebrity lived his life as a (**mien, recluse**), permanently turning his back on public life.

12. The injured quarterback (**chafed, encroached**) at sitting on the bench while his team was being badly beaten on the field.

Completing the Sentence

Choose the word from the word bank that best completes each of the following sentences. Write the correct word or form of the word in the space provided.

awry	chafe	encroach	mien	predominant
bludgeon	dire	fend	penal	recluse

1. As the jurors filed back into the courtroom, their stern _____ alarmed the defendants.

2. Let us hope that scientists are wrong in their _____ predictions that there will be a major earthquake in our region.

3. The Scottish poet Robert Burns reminds us that no matter how carefully we plan, things may still go _____.

4. True, I wanted to make some money, but my _____ reason for taking the job was that I needed practical work experience.

5. Do you believe that the crime rate will go down if the _____ code is made more severe?

6. The parents promised that they would not meddle with or _____ on the privacy of their married children.

7. To carry out his great work, he chose to separate himself from society and live the solitary life of a(n) _____.

8. Shoes that will not _____ your feet are the most important piece of equipment you will need for a hike.

9. When his efforts to _____ off the bill collectors proved unsuccessful, my uncle was forced to declare bankruptcy.

10. Some people have the unpleasant habit of verbally _____ their opponents in an argument by loudly repeating a single phrase.

Definitions

Note the spelling, pronunciation, part(s) of speech, and definition(s) of each of the following words. Then write the appropriate form of the word in the blank space in the illustrative sentence(s) following.

1. apt
(apt)

(*adj.*) suitable, fitting, likely; quick to learn
　　The appropriate greeting card for a particular occasion is one that expresses _____ sentiments.

2. capitulate
(kə pich′ ə lāt)

(*v.*) to end resistance, give up, throw in the towel
　　When I saw that I had been outmaneuvered by my opponent, I had no choice but to _____.

3. defile
(di fīl′)

(*v., trans.*) to make unclean or dirty, destroy the purity of; (*v., intrans.*) to march in a single line or in columns; (*n.*) a narrow passage; gorge, canyon
　　Those who _____ a house of worship will be punished to the full extent of the law.
　　The victorious troops _____ for review.
　　We hiked through the rocky _____.

4. disarming
(dis ärm′ iŋ)

(*adj.*) charming, tending to soften unfriendliness or suspicion
　　My best friend has a most _____ smile.

5. disgruntled
(dis grənt′ əld)

(*adj., part*) in bad humor, discontented, annoyed
　　When flights are delayed because of bad weather, airline passengers may become extremely _____.

6. endow
(en dau′)

(*v.*) to furnish, equip, provide with funds or some other desirable thing or quality
　　Wealthy individuals often make provisions in their wills to _____ their favorite charities.

7. impunity
(im pyü′ nə tē)

(*n.*) freedom from punishment
　　Bullies must be made to realize that they cannot push other people around with _____.

8. pertinent
(pər′ tə nənt)

(*adj.*) related to the matter at hand, to the point
　　The joke you told was very amusing, but I fail to see how it was _____ to the conversation.

9. prodigy
(präd′ ə jē)

(*n.*) something wonderful or marvelous; an unusual feat; a child or young person with extraordinary ability or talent

The careers of some musical _____ have turned out to be short-lived.

10. renown
(ri naủn′)

(*n.*) fame, glory

Some writers earn acclaim during their lifetime, but others win _____ only after their death.

Using Context

*For each item, determine whether the **boldface** word from pages 130–131 makes sense in the context of the sentence. Circle the item numbers next to the six sentences in which the words are used correctly.*

1. I decided to create an organizational system in order to **defile** the mess of documents that sat on my desk.

2. Many students wondered why they saw a preteen girl around the university campus, until they learned that she was a **prodigy** in mathematics and was taking advanced classes.

3. The heat and humidity that morning were **apt** to make many people drop out of the race.

4. The **impunity** with which he reacted to someone teasing him good-naturedly showed us all that he cannot take a joke.

5. Those with **disarming** dispositions often make excellent salespeople, as they can easily win people's trust.

6. While the young girl is a talented dancer, she prefers to do it as a hobby and would never seek **renown** by performing publicly.

7. I attempted to **capitulate** the interview with the businessman by asking some follow-up questions, but his assistant led him away to another engagement.

8. Rather than spending her wealth on material goods, the famous actress decided to **endow** her former college with the funds they would need to build a new auditorium.

9. Her **pertinent** remarks showed that she did not know as much about the subject as she claimed to beforehand.

10. The customer service department spent the day dealing with **disgruntled** customers whose packages had not arrived on time because of a snowstorm.

Choosing the Right Word

Select the **boldface** word that better completes each sentence. You might refer to the passage on pages 124–125 to see how most of these words are used in context. Note that the choices might be related forms of the Unit words.

1. Some great composers, including Mozart and Mendelssohn, were (**pertinent, apt**) musicians from a very early age, demonstrating an amazing talent for writing music.

2. When the featured singer failed to appear, the (**disgruntled, apt**) fans demanded their money back.

3. Nature is kind to us in many ways, but we must learn that we cannot violate its laws with (**impunity, renown**).

4. Marie is (**apt, endowed**) to forget where she puts important things, such as her keys, wallet, and glasses.

5. The message of a great work of literature may be as (**pertinent, disgruntled**) today as it was when it was first written.

6. Although the child was terrified of shots, the skillful nurse (**capitulated, disarmed**) the weeping boy by singing a funny song.

7. Alvin York performed such (**impunities, prodigies**) on the battlefields of France that he was awarded this nation's highest honors.

8. The Declaration of Independence mentions a number of "unalienable rights" with which all people "are (**endowed, capitulated**) by their Creator."

9. I was so (**capitulated, disarmed**) by the way he asked for a loan that to my surprise I found myself giving him the money.

10. He claims to be a patriot, but his disregard for the powerless (**endows, defiles**) the great ideals on which this nation was built.

11. A team as determined as ours is will never (**capitulate, endow**), even if it is losing badly in the final moments of a game.

12. The college my sister attends is a small one, but it has gained a great deal of (**impunity, renown**) for the quality of its faculty.

Completing the Sentence

Choose the word from the word bank that best completes each of the following sentences. Write the correct word or form of the word in the space provided.

apt	**defile**	**disgruntled**	**impunity**	**prodigy**
capitulate	**disarming**	**endow**	**pertinent**	**renown**

1. The brave soldiers defending the fort _____ only when they realized that further resistance was useless.

2. Even though you are _____ because the candidate you favored did not win the nomination, you should still vote in the election.

3. Even before Martin Luther King, Jr., won the Nobel Peace Prize in 1964, his _____ had spread throughout most of the world.

4. We were prepared to make an angry complaint to the salesclerk, but her _____ manner soon put us in a friendlier mood.

5. In your answers, be precise and try to give only the details that you know are _____ to this investigation.

6. It is up to you to make good use of the talents with which nature has seen fit to _____ you.

7. There's an old saying that tells us that if you walk like a duck and talk like a duck, people are _____ to take you for a duck.

8. In my opinion, the countryside is _____ by billboards that block our view of the beauties of nature.

9. We were amazed that the large, fierce-looking dog allowed the child to pull its tail with _____.

10. The Grand Canyon and Niagara Falls are considered by many to be awe-inspiring _____ of nature.

Synonyms

*Choose the word or form of the word from this Unit that is the same or most nearly the same in meaning as the **boldface** word or expression in the phrase. Write that word on the line. Use a dictionary if necessary.*

1. paid a **proper** tribute _____
2. had a reputation of being a **loner** _____
3. trespassed with apparent **amnesty** _____
4. fought their attempts to **invade** our privacy _____
5. was an award-winning tennis **marvel** _____
6. came to the fight armed with a **club** _____
7. an **endearing** smile _____
8. an attitude that was **prevalent** during the Victorian age _____
9. **stave off** the pickpocket _____
10. a gruff **demeanor** but a kindly heart _____
11. issued an **ominous** forecast _____
12. **gave up** after a long and exhausting struggle _____
13. further **aggravated** our already strained nerves _____
14. obtain all the **relevant** documents _____
15. sent the defendant to a **correctional** facility _____

Antonyms

*Choose the word or form of the word from this Unit that is most nearly opposite in meaning to the **boldface** word or expression in the phrase. Write that word on the line. Use a dictionary if necessary.*

1. to **revere** the natural beauty _____
2. due to the **obscurity** of the film _____
3. was **deprived** of a good sense of humor _____
4. a **satisfied** customer _____
5. sensed that things were **in order** _____

Writing: Words in Action

Think about what Tecumseh did for his people. Write a tribute to Tecumseh, describing how he positively affected the lives of the Shawnee. Use examples from your reading (pages 124–125), personal experiences, and prior knowledge. Use three or more words from this Unit.

Vocabulary in Context

*Some of the words you have studied in this Unit appear in **boldface** type. Read the passage below, and then circle the letter of the correct answer for each word as it is used in context.*

Corn has long been the key ingredient in the diet of Native Americans. And Native people fashioned dolls for their children made from the husks of corn. The dolls were simple, just corn husks, or they were more elaborate, sporting clothes and holding **apt** tools such as cooking utensils or canoe paddles. But these dolls typically lacked faces.

Each tribe has a **pertinent** yet slightly different legend surrounding these faceless dolls. The Iroquois legend, for instance, says that the Great Spirit gave the Corn Spirit permission to create a corn-husk doll with a beautiful face, but the corn-husk doll grew too vain. The Great Spirit warned the corn-husk doll she was committing a **penal** offense and spoke of **dire** consequences if she did not change her ways. The doll continued to admire her reflection in pools of water, and continued to be vain. As punishment for ignoring the Great Spirit, the legend goes, the Great Spirit did not **defile** her face. Instead he took it away completely.

In keeping with their tradition of not wasting natural resources, Native Americans used up every part of the ears of corn. Corn husks were braided to make rope, baskets, mats, and rugs, or transformed into moccasins and other clothing. Corn cobs were used as fuel. When the first European settlers came to America, Native people introduced them to corn and taught them how to grow it. They also showed them how to make corn-husk dolls, and the settlers adopted the tradition. Then, even children as shy as a **recluse** embraced the dolls as comforting friends.

---

1. What is the meaning of **apt** as it is used in paragraph 1?
   a. fitting
   b. lightweight
   c. feminine
   d. popular

2. The word **pertinent** means about the same as
   a. unusual
   b. relevant
   c. remarkable
   d. tragic

3. What is the meaning of **penal** as it is used in paragraph 2?
   a. unwritten
   b. visible
   c. disciplinary
   d. foolish

4. **Dire** comes from the Latin word **dirus**. **Dirus** most likely means
   a. absolute
   b. fearsome
   c. distinct
   d. direct

5. What is the meaning of **defile** as it is used in paragraph 2?
   a. to question directly
   b. to disobey an order
   c. to destroy the purity of
   d. to threaten the life of

6. In paragraph 3, what does the use of the word **recluse** suggest about the children?
   a. They are withdrawn.
   b. They are difficult.
   c. They have friends.
   d. They are lovable.

Vocabulary for Comprehension
Part 1

*Read "The Queen's Twin," which contains words in **boldface** that appear in Units 7–9. Then answer the questions.*

The Queen's Twin
by Sarah Orne Jewett

Before us lay a splendid world of sea and shore. The autumn colors already brightened the landscape; and here and there at the edge of a dark tract of pointed
(5) firs stood a row of bright swamp-maples. The blue sea and the great tide inlets were untroubled by the lightest winds.

"Poor land, this is!" sighed Mrs. Todd as we sat down to rest on the worn doorstep.
(10) "I've known three good hard-workin' families that come here full o' hope an' pride and tried to make something o' this farm, but it beat 'em all. There's one small field that's excellent for potatoes if you
(15) let half of it rest every year; but the land's always hungry. Now, you see them little peakéd-topped spruces an' fir balsams comin' up over the hill all green an' hearty; they've got it all their own way! Seems
(20) sometimes as if wild Natur' got jealous over a certain spot, and wanted to do just as she'd a mind to. You'll see here; she'll do her own ploughin' an' harrowin' with frost an' wet, an' plant just what she wants
(25) and wait for her own crops. Man can't do nothin' with it, try as he may."

I looked down the slope, and felt as if we ourselves were likely to be overcome if we lingered too long. There was a **fervent**
(30) vigor of growth, a persistence and a **perceptible** savagery about the sturdy little trees which suggested that powerful wild Nature and frail human nature were in a state of complete **enmity**. One felt
(35) a sudden pity for the **stoical** and unassuming men and women whose unflagging efforts had been nullified

after a long fight in that lonely place; their labors had been to no **avail**. One felt fear
(40) of the unconquerable forces of Nature.

"I can recollect the time when folks were shy o' these woods we just come through," said Mrs. Todd seriously. "The men-folks themselves never'd venture into
(45) 'em alone; if their cattle got strayed they'd collect whoever they could get, and start off all together. They said a person was liable to get bewildered in there alone, and in old times folks had been lost. I
(50) expect there was considerable fear left over from the old times. Some people don't seem able to **fend** it off; I've seen bold men act kind o' timid. Some women o' the Asa Bowden family went out one
(55) afternoon berryin' when I was a girl, and got lost and was out all night; they found 'em middle o' the mornin' next day, not half a mile from home, scared most to death, an' sayin' they'd heard wolves and
(60) other beasts sufficient for a caravan. Poor creatur's! they'd strayed at last into a kind of low place amongst some alders, an' one of 'em was so overset she never got over it, an' went off in a sort o' slow
(65) decline. 'Twas like them victims that drowns in a foot o' water; but their minds did suffer dreadful. Some folks is born afraid of the woods and all wild places, but I must say they've always been like
(70) home to me."

1. Which sentence **best** summarizes the first paragraph?
   A) Fine fall weather and tranquil coastal waters promise a perfect day for a walk.
   B) The narrator surveys the beauty of the coastal landscape on a fall day.
   C) Dramatic irony permits the reader to understand features of the landscape.
   D) The author introduces her major theme.

2. According to the line 29, what is **fervent** vigor?
   A) flushed
   B) increasing
   C) unhealthy
   D) intense

3. What is the meaning of **perceptible** as it is used in line 31?
   A) hardworking
   B) noticeable
   C) patient
   D) uncaring

4. As it is used in line 34, what is the meaning of **enmity**?
   A) friendship
   B) hostility
   C) impatient
   D) unwholesome

5. According to line 35, what are **stoical** men and women?
   A) hardworking
   B) heroic
   C) self-controlled
   D) uncaring

6. What is the meaning of **avail** as it is used in line 39?
   A) effect
   B) profit
   C) purpose
   D) end

7. Which phrase is closest in meaning to **fend** as it is used in line 52?
   A) to settle on
   B) to nourish
   C) to ward off
   D) to work hard

8. Which sentence would be included in a summary of lines 41–67?
   A) Fears, superstitions, and mysterious events were connected with the woods.
   B) Mrs. Todd has personal reasons for not entering the woods at night.
   C) It is a history of the woods and of other wild places in the surrounding area.
   D) Mrs. Todd explains people's failure to farm the land near the woods.

9. **Part A**
   Which inference about Mrs. Todd is supported by the text?
   A) She is afraid of wild nature.
   B) She is courageous in the woods.
   C) She intends to frighten the narrator.
   D) She is unafraid of the woods.

   Part B
   Which evidence from *The Queen's Twin* supports the answer to Part A?
   A) "she'll do her own ploughin' an' harrowin'" (lines 22–23)
   B) "fear of the unconquerable forces of Nature" (lines 39–40)
   C) "a person was liable to get bewildered in there" (lines 47–48)
   D) " they've always been like home to me" (lines 69–70)

10. Which lines from *The Queen's Twin* **best** states the passage's central idea?
    A) "Before us lay a splendid world of sea and shore" (lines 1–2)
    B) "wild Natur' got jealous over a certain spot" (lines 20–21)
    C) "powerful wild Nature and frail human nature were in a state of complete enmity" (lines 32–34)
    D) "a person was liable to get bewildered in there alone, and in old times folks had been lost" (lines 47–49)

Vocabulary for Comprehension

Part 2

*Read this passages, which contain words in **boldface** that appear in Units 7–9. Then choose the best answer to each question based on what is stated or implied in the passage(s). You may refer to the passages as often as necessary.*

Questions 1–10 are based on the following passage.

This passage is adapted from *Arthur Mervyn; or, Memoirs of the Year 1793* by Charles Brockden Brown. Originally published 1779.

Having already been cheated out of all the money I had set out with, once I was within the city I kept to the side-streets. By the time I reached Market Street night

(5) had fallen, and a triple row of lamps presented a spectacle enchanting and new. My personal cares were, for a time, lost in the tumultuous sensations that suddenly crowded in on me. I had never

(10) before visited the city at this hour. I had last come to the city as a mere child. The novelty of everything I encountered was, therefore, nearly absolute. I proceeded with cautious steps, but was still absorbed

(15) in attention to every passing object.

I reached the market-house, and, entering it, immersed myself in new delight and new wonder. I need not remark that our ideas of magnificence and splendour

(20) are merely comparative, but I am sure you will smile when I tell you that, as I was walking through this avenue with its starry lamps and blazing crescents, I imagined for a moment that I had been **conveyed** to

(25) the infernal regions, which are not dark as some people imagine, but, as I recall from John Milton's *Paradise Lost*, are bathed in dazzling brilliance at all times of the day and night. That it had taken so few hours

(30) to discover this new world, at so little distance from the rural quiet of my own home, seemed magical.

At the **juncture** of Market Street and Front Street I sat down on a bench to rest.

(35) I could no longer **parry** the effects of the long journey. Even though I was accustomed to strenuous exertion it was no wonder that I felt great fatigue; I had travelled forty-five miles in the last fifteen

(40) hours. I took a deep breath and began to think seriously about my situation. I was a stranger, friendless and moneyless. I was unable to purchase food and shelter, and was wholly unused to the business of

(45) being a beggar and a **scavenger**. I had no objection to spending the night in the spot where I then sat, and I was certain that I would be allowed to sleep with **impunity**. It was no crime to be without

(50) a home; but how was I going to satisfy my appetite, which would be so much sharper tomorrow?

At length it occurred to me that John Fawley, one of our closest country

(55) neighbors, might be in the city at this moment. As well as running a farm, he owned a store in the city. He was a plain and well-meaning man with many fine **attributes**, and, should I be so fortunate

(60) as to meet him, his superior knowledge of the city might help me out of my present difficulties, and his generosity might lead him to buy me a meal.

I had already decided to **capitulate**,

(65) and to leave the city the next day. As I sat there cold and hungry, **chafing** my hands, I was astonished at the folly that had led me there. In the meantime, however, I had to eat. Where should I look for John Fawley?

(70) I remembered him once saying that when he was in the city he stayed at an inn. He had even mentioned its name, but, for the time being at least, I could not recall it. My resolution began to **waver**.

1. It can reasonably be inferred that the narrator initially stays off the city's main streets
A) because he was nervous that he might be robbed once more.
B) because he is ashamed of being seen by people.
C) in order to avoid being tempted by things he cannot afford.
D) because he is nervous that he might lose his way.

2. The narrator's momentary impression that he had been carried to the "infernal regions" helps to convey the idea that
A) the narrator has a good imagination.
B) the city might not be a good place.
C) the narrator might not be human.
D) the narrator is a lost soul.

3. As it is used in line 33, "juncture" most nearly means
A) joining.
B) corner.
C) dead-end.
D) fork.

4. As it is used in line 45, "scavenger" most nearly means
A) someone who roams unseen through densely-populated environments.
B) a person who lives on vegetables and fruit stolen from farms.
C) someone who searches discarded items for something useful.
D) a person who lies in wait to accost unwary members of the public.

5. It can reasonably be inferred from the passage that the narrator is
A) naive and uneducated.
B) wicked and unnatural.
C) educated and gentle.
D) cunning and resourceful.

6. As it is used in line 49, "impunity" most nearly means
A) freedom.
B) security.
C) risk.
D) allowance.

7. Which choice provides the best evidence for the answer to the previous question?
A) Lines 33–34 ("At the juncture ... rest")
B) Lines 49–50 ("It was ... home")
C) Lines 57–63 ("He was a ... meal")
D) Lines 65–68 ("As I ... there")

8. As it is used in line 59, "attributes" most nearly means
A) accessories.
B) possessions.
C) traits.
D) faults.

9. It can reasonably be inferred from the final paragraph that the narrator is
A) unsure what to do.
B) remorseful for his actions.
C) remorseless and arrogant.
D) resolute and determined.

10. Which of the following sentences best summarizes the passage?
A) A man with a mysterious past comes to the city destitute and decides to live by his wits alone.
B) A young man from the country arrives penniless in the city and must decide whether to stay and take his chances or leave the city.
C) A country bumpkin is robbed on his way to the city, and decides to beg a meal from a neighboring farmer before he goes back home.
D) A young woman from the country considers whether to call on an old friend while she is visiting the city.

Synonyms

*From the word bank below, choose the word that has the same or nearly the same meaning as the **boldface** word in each sentence and write it on the line. You will not use all of the words.*

apt	capitulate	perceptible	scavenger
avail	dire	pertinent	stoical
awry	excise	predominant	turncoat
bludgeon	penal	proxy	unflagging

1. The meteorologist's **urgent** warnings to evacuate before the hurricane seemed overly dramatic after nothing more than a light rainfall occurred. _____

2. Although I do like baseball, my **chief** reason for joining the team was to get some more exercise. _____

3. On his graduation day, he wrote his parents a thank-you note for their **steady** support and encouragement throughout his education. _____

4. The school's **disciplinary** code makes clear that anyone who is late to school on a regular basis must go to detention. _____

5. At her retirement party, she tried to remain **self-controlled** but she was soon crying tears of gratitude. _____

6. It seems unfair that my former teammates would call me a **deserter** for joining the baseball team at my new school. _____

7. I left the curtains I no longer wanted on the sidewalk by the trash, knowing that some **rummager** would come along and take them. _____

8. The entrepreneurs struggled to think of an **appropriate** name for their business that reflected the services they offered. _____

9. After I have written an essay, I review it and **cut out** any words or phrases I might have overused. _____

10. There was a **noticeable** difference in his mood after he received his graded test, suggesting that he did better than he'd expected. _____

11. "Please save any conversation that is not **relevant** to this discussion for after class," the teacher said, directing her gaze at me. _____

12. His tendency to **clobber** his opponents with different forms of the same argument comes across as lazy and combative. _____

Two-Word Completions

Select the pair of words that best completes the meaning of each of the following sentences.

1. At first, I was perfectly content to do the rather _____ tasks that my summer job involved. But as time went on, I became thoroughly _____ with such undemanding and unpleasant assignments.
a. menial … disgruntled
b. tawdry … intrigued
c. exotic … obsessed
d. unassuming … endowed

2. Though they never seem to think alike on any subject, there isn't the slightest hint of _____ between them. I think it's not uncommon for two people whose views _____ so sharply to dislike one another intensely.
a. impunity … encroach
b. doctrine … nullify
c. enmity … diverge
d. juncture … abut

3. The old adage that clothes often _____ the man simply means that a person's _____ is frequently a kind of public statement about his or her personality.
a. defile … stance
b. proclaim … attire
c. convey … renown
d. attribute … mien

4. Struck by a dreadful disease, my friend became a shadow of her former self. I did not at first recognize the _____ figure that lay in the bed before me. Her once carefree face was now drawn and _____.
a. ravaged … disarming
b. cryptic … jaunty
c. stinted … fervent
d. gaunt … haggard

5. For a while the politician stood high in public favor, but then his reputation suddenly _____ to earth. One day he was basking in the sunshine of popular approval; the next he found himself _____ under the yoke of universal disfavor.
a. belittled … rankling
b. parried … wallowing
c. plummeted … chafing
d. wavered … encroaching

6. During the deciding game, the challenger, a 12-year-old _____ by the name of Mikie, _____ the moves of the champion, herself a grand master and chess authority, with the expertise of an accomplished veteran.
a. acme … fended off
b. recluse … nullified
c. crony … belittled
d. prodigy … parried

7. The wolf, a _____ creature that eats other animals, is often viewed as a threat to ranchers. Presently, the grey wolf has been designated an endangered species, and its most serious threat is human _____ into wolf territory.
a. menial … infiltration
b. predatory … encroachment
c. fervent … impunity
d. disarming … attribution

WORD STUDY

Idioms

In the passage about Toni Cade Bambara (see pages 56–57), the narrator describes one of Bambara's characters, Squeaky. The narrator states that although Squeaky enjoyed a wealth of wisdom, she was not born on "Easy Street." What the narrator means is that Squeaky's life was not an easy one.

"Easy Street" is an idiom that refers to a life of comfort or material wealth. An **idiom** is an everyday expression that should be understood figuratively, not literally. Some idioms are particular to a certain region or culture, while others are used more universally. Every language has its own idioms.

Choosing the Right Idiom

Read each sentence. Use context clues to figure out the meaning of each idiom in **boldface** *print. Then write the letter of the definition for the idiom in the sentence.*

1. Glenn wants to run for mayor, but many think he's still **wet behind the ears**. _____

2. My grandpa likes to spend time at the coffee shop **chewing the fat** with the neighbors. _____

3. The Wilsons needed more **elbow room** and so moved into a bigger home. _____

4. If you haven't heard the news, you must be **living under a rock**. _____

5. I would really like to help you, but **my hands are tied** and there is nothing I can do. _____

6. "Don't worry about losing your job; I've **got your back**," Liam said. _____

7. When confronted with electrical and plumbing problems, Benny realized he was **in over his head** with the kitchen remodel. _____

8. Only a driver with **eagle eyes** can find a parking space at the mall during the holidays. _____

9. When the rest of the clean-up crew left without notice, Jill was **left holding the bag**. _____

10. Lori volunteered for everything this summer, and I fear she **spread herself too thin**. _____

a. left to complete something that was another person's responsibility

b. took on too many obligations

c. looking out for someone's welfare; supporting a friend

d. having casual conversation

e. adequate space to move about

f. challenged by a task beyond one's ability or means

g. unable to act due to restrictions

h. unaware of what's going on in the world

i. keen vision

j. young and inexperienced

Classical Roots

chron—time; **cryph, crypt**—hidden, secret

The Greek root **chron** means "time" The root **cryph** or **crypt** appears in **cryptic** (page 118), meaning "puzzling or mystifying." Some other words based on these roots are listed below.

anachronism	chronic	chronological	encrypt
apocryphal	crypt	cryptogram	synchronize

From the list of words above, choose the one that corresponds to each of the brief definitions below. Write the word in the blank space in the illustrative sentence below the definition. Use a dictionary if necessary.

1. something that is out of its proper time
A telephone would be a(n) _____ in a movie set in colonial times.

2. to occur at the same time
Pairs skaters must _____ their movements so that they execute their routines in unison.

3. something written in a code to conceal its meaning, a cipher
Army intelligence intercepted an enemy _____.

4. of questionable authorship or authenticity, false, counterfeit
Many tales of the exploits of Daniel Boone and Davy Crockett are probably
_____.

5. of long duration, continuing; constant
Drought is a(n) _____ problem in many parts of the world.

6. arranged in the order of time of occurrence
A ship captain's log provides a(n) _____ record of a voyage.

7. an underground vault or chamber, often used for burial
Colorful paintings adorned the walls of the pharaoh's _____.

8. to convert a message into a code or cipher
Prisoners sometimes try to _____ pleas for help in their letters.

Read the following passage, taking note of the **boldface** words and their contexts. These words are among those you will be studying in Unit 10. It may help you to complete the exercises in this Unit if you refer to the way the words are used below.

The Adventures of Narváez and Cabeza de Vaca in the New World

<Historical Nonfiction>

On June 17, 1527, the Narváez expedition departed from Spain to claim Florida for the Spanish crown. By this time, Spain's **transition** from European kingdom to global empire was well underway. The Spanish were experienced seafarers and colonizers, and by all accounts, the Narváez expedition was **devised** in **accord** with the best practices of the day. The risks **entailed** in such ventures remained high, however. The Narváez expedition was a **veritable** disaster.

Five ships set out that day, carrying 600 men led by the conquistador Pánfilo de Narváez. After three months at sea, the fleet landed on the island of Hispaniola. While the officers procured horses and ships, about 100 men deserted. Weeks later, the expedition arrived at Cuba. At least 80 men, two ships, and many supplies were lost to a hurricane. More bad weather **vexed** the fleet as it sailed around the Cuban coast, and **dexterous** navigation proved no match for the elements.

The battered fleet reached the Florida coast in April 1528, with a crew of about 400 men. They **bartered** with the native villagers, exchanging beads and cloth for food. The villagers must have felt some **trepidation** at the Spaniards' arrival, as they abandoned the village overnight. The Spaniards soon encountered another village, where they heard rumors of gold to the north. Narváez decided to split the party, sending 300 men north by land to **ferret** out the rumored gold, and the rest to sail up the coast. One officer, Alvar Núñez Cabeza de Vaca, argued that it would be wiser to keep the group together. Narváez overruled the dissenter and **upbraided** him with a **curt** reply, accusing him of cowardice. It was a rash decision that the travelers would come to **rue**, but they knew little then of the **impending** challenges.

The 300 men who headed north never saw their ships again. They encountered hospitable villagers who supplied them with food, but they found no cities of gold. Drained of **vitality** by guerrilla attacks, food shortages, and disease, the expedition returned south. There, the exhausted men built crude boats, hoping to reach Spanish settlements in Mexico. Most of the men, including Narváez, died during this desperate journey. About 80 men, including Cabeza de Vaca, landed on an island inhabited by the Karankawa tribe, who enslaved the Spaniards. After a harsh winter, only 15 members of the expedition remained. They learned to live among the Karankawa as captive medicine men, practicing the art of healing, moving with their captors between the island and the mainland. When in Rome, do as the Romans do.

Unable to convince the other Spaniards to escape, Cabeza de Vaca set off on his own into the wilderness. He roamed some 150 miles along the coast, making a living as a trader. In the summer of 1532, he encountered three other survivors of the expedition, who were slaves of a local tribe. Cabeza de Vaca joined these men in captivity, and the four planned their escape. Their chance came in the spring of 1535. While their captors were **engrossed** in a feast, the four Spaniards escaped into the desert and headed south for the Rio Grande. Months later, they stumbled upon a party of Spanish slave-hunters, who led them to Mexico City. Nearly nine years after the Narváez expedition had set out from Spain, the journey of these four final survivors had finally reached its end.

Audio

For iWords and audio passages, go to SadlierConnect.com.

Definitions

Note the spelling, pronunciation, part(s) of speech, and definition(s) of each of the following words. Then write the appropriate form of the word in the blank space in the illustrative sentence(s) following.

1. accord
(ə kôrd')

(*n.*) agreement, harmony; (*v.*) to agree, be in harmony or bring into harmony; to grant, bestow on

The labor union reached an _____ with management before the midnight deadline.

The Nobel Committee _____ the Peace Prize to the Red Cross in 1917, 1944, and 1963.

2. curt
(kərt)

(*adj.*) short, rudely brief

Tour guides are trained to give complete and polite answers to questions, not _____ responses.

3. engross
(en grōs')

(*v.*) to occupy the complete attention of, absorb fully

The exciting new film _____ every member of the audience.

4. entail
(*v.*, en tāl';
n., en' tāl)

(*v.*) to put a burden on, impose, involve; to restrict ownership of property by limiting inheritance; (*n.*) such a restriction

Reaching your goals will _____ both hard work and sacrifice.

By tradition, an _____ requires that our great-grandmother's paintings must pass to the oldest child.

5. impending
(im pen' diŋ)

(*adj., part.*) about to happen, hanging over in a menacing way

If you have studied hard, you have no reason to worry about your _____ final exams.

6. rue
(rü)

(*v.*) to regret, be sorry for; (*n.*) a feeling of regret

It is only natural to _____ mistakes and missed opportunities.

My heart was filled with _____ when I realized how thoughtlessly I had behaved.

7. transition
(tran zish' ən)

(*n.*) a change from one state or condition to another

Because of a change in leadership, the country is undergoing a period of political _____.

8. upbraid
(əp brād')

(v.) to blame, scold, find fault with
The police officer _____ the driver for blocking the crosswalk.

9. veritable
(ver' ə tə bəl)

(adj.) actual, true, real
Those dusty old boxes in my grandparents' attic contained a _____ treasure trove of rare books and valuable antiques.

10. vitality
(vī tal' ə tē)

(n.) strength, energy; the capacity to live and develop; the power to endure or survive
To win a marathon, a runner must have patience, speed, and exceptional _____.

Using Context

*For each item, determine whether the **boldface** word from pages 146–147 makes sense in the context of the sentence. Circle the item numbers next to the six sentences in which the words are used correctly.*

1. When you consult and list sources for a research paper, you must be sure of their **vitality**.

2. These workshops, which are offered throughout the year, are designed to help students successfully make the **transition** from high school to college.

3. According to experts, a dark-green, leafy vegetable, such as kale or spinach, is a **veritable** powerhouse of good nutrition.

4. The signing of an **accord** in 1992 paved the way for the establishment of Nunavut, a new territory of Canada that would have its own government.

5. It's nice to see that simple toys such as model trains and building blocks still have the power to **engross** young children and engage them in hours of imaginative play.

6. Although my injury is not serious, it will **entail** my participation in sports for a month.

7. Employees were worried that the **impending** sale of the company would affect their jobs.

8. Several of the poems in this section of the anthology can be described as expressions of **rue** over the brevity of life.

9. You must make sure that your skates have **curt** edges; otherwise they will not grip the ice.

10. We visited the nursing home to perform a concert to **upbraid** the residents.

Choosing the Right Word

*Select the **boldface** word that better completes each sentence. You might refer to the passage on pages 144–145 to see how most of these words are used in context. Note that the choices might be related forms of the Unit words.*

1. Rachel Carson hoped her book *Silent Spring* would prompt people to be in (**accord, transition**) with her view on the use of insecticides.

2. A long series of minor illnesses sapped his (**vitality, transition**), leaving him unable to work.

3. My uncle told me that dropping out of school at an early age was a decision he has always (**rued, engrossed**).

4. The (**vitality, transition**) from country living to city living was more difficult than I imagined.

5. The years of adolescence mark the (**transition, accord**) from childhood to adulthood.

6. Our science teacher (**entailed, upbraided**) us when we failed to follow proper safety precautions in the lab.

7. Millions of people, not only in India but in all parts of the world, came to regard Gandhi as a (**veritable, curt**) saint.

8. The telegram contained a(n) (**impending, curt**) message ordering me to return home as soon as possible.

9. As the screaming fans stormed the stadium, security prepared for an (**upbraided, impending**) riot.

10. You may find it hard to become (**engrossed, upbraided**) in the study of irregular verbs, but you'll have to master them if you want to learn French.

11. When we moved from an apartment to a house, we found that being homeowners (**entails, rues**) more responsibilities than we had imagined.

12. The mayor warned of a(n) (**curt, impending**) crisis unless measures are taken immediately to conserve the city's water supply.

Completing the Sentence

Choose the word from the word bank that best completes each of the following sentences. Write the correct word or form of the word in the space provided.

accord	engross	impending	transition	veritable
curt	entail	rue	upbraid	vitality

1. Before applying for that job, you should know that it _____ late-night and early-morning shifts.

2. I assure you that you will _____ the day you challenged us to a karaoke contest.

3. During the twentieth century, many countries in Africa and Asia made the _____ from colonial status to national independence.

4. One doesn't have to be a weather specialist to know that a darkening sky is a sign of a(n) _____ storm.

5. Every time I go to the dentist, she _____ me for eating things that are bad for my teeth.

6. The project I was working on _____ me so thoroughly that I forgot to stop for lunch.

7. I don't expect long explanations, but why must his answers to my questions be so _____?

8. During those difficult years, the state was in the hands of a do-nothing administration completely lacking in _____ and direction.

9. The firefighters who rescued three families from a burning building fully deserve all the honors _____ them.

10. Since the artist seems to have known everyone of importance in her time, her diaries read like a(n) _____ *Who's Who* of the period.

Definitions

Note the spelling, pronunciation, part(s) of speech, and definition(s) of each of the following words. Then write the appropriate form of the word in the blank space in the illustrative sentence(s) following.

---

1. barter
(bär′ tər)

(*n.*) an exchange in trade; (*v.*) to exchange goods
By definition, _____ does not involve the exchange of money in any form.
According to the Hebrew Bible, Esau, the brother of Jacob, _____ away his birthright for a hot meal.

---

2. devise
(di vīz′)

(*v.*) to think out, plan, figure out, invent, create
The advertising agency _____ clever commercials promoting the new car.

---

3. dexterous
(dek′ strəs)

(*adj.*) skillful in the use of hands or body; clever
The _____ movements of those master chefs we see on TV took years of practice to perfect.

---

4. ferret
(fer′ ət)

(*n.*) a kind of weasel; (*v.*) to search or hunt out; to torment, badger
_____ were once used to chase rabbits and other pests from their burrows.
No matter how long it takes, we'll keep asking questions until we _____ out the true story.

---

5. habituate
(hə bich′ ü āt)

(*v.*) to become used to; to cause to become used to
Rookies who quickly _____ themselves to discipline can make important contributions to a team.

---

6. personable
(pərs′ nə bəl)

(*adj.*) pleasing in appearance or personality, attractive
A group of very _____ and enthusiastic teens volunteered to help senior citizens with daily chores.

---

7. scoff
(skäf)

(*v.*) to make fun of; to show contempt for
People once _____ at the notion that the use of personal computers would become widespread.

---

8. trepidation
(trep ə dā′ shən)

(*n.*) fear, fright, trembling
Even veteran actors experience _____ just before they go on stage.

---

9. **vex**
(veks)

(v.) to annoy, anger, exasperate; to confuse, baffle

The annual task of filling out federal and state income tax returns _____ many people.

10. **whimsical**
(whim′ zə kəl)

(adj.) subject to odd ideas, notions, or fancies; playful; unpredictable

Rube Goldberg was famous for _____ drawings of wildly impractical contraptions.

Using Context

*For each item, determine whether the **boldface** word from pages 150–151 makes sense in the context of the sentence. Circle the item numbers next to the six sentences in which the words are used correctly.*

1. After hours of trying to **devise** a plan to raise money for the library, the group agreed to have a used book sale.

2. Just when it seemed like the rain would never end, the drops began to slowly **habituate** and we saw rays of sun peeking through the clouds.

3. The investigative reporter is known for her ability to **ferret** out the truth from even the most unwilling of subjects.

4. That salesman seems to have the power to **vex** every customer that walks through the door, as his clients rarely leave without purchasing a brand new car.

5. While I'm sure the famous doctor is skilled at what he does, he was not especially **personable** and I didn't feel at ease in his company.

6. After a day grounded in reality, I sometimes like to escape by reading a **whimsical** fairy tale that transports me to another world.

7. Everyone in the audience was entranced by the **dexterous** voice of the company's new lead soprano.

8. Those who **scoff** at the ambitious goals of others are usually too insecure to have high hopes for themselves.

9. The shopkeeper refused to let the customer **barter** wheat from her farm for the valuable jewelry, insisting that they were not of equal value.

10. I was nearly shaking with **trepidation** before the big party, so excited and giddy to catch up with friends I hadn't seen in years.

Choosing the Right Word

*Select the **boldface** word that better completes each sentence. You might refer to the passage on pages 144–145 to see how most of these words are used in context. Note that the choices might be related forms of the Unit words.*

1. During the oil crisis of the 1970s, Americans had to (**habituate, vex**) themselves to lower indoor temperatures and decreased use of private transportation.

2. Good office managers must be (**dexterous, whimsical**) in using their powers to meet goals without discouraging employees.

3. Do not (**scoff, barter**) at him because he wants to be a good student.

4. Presidents need capable assistants who will shield them from minor problems that may (**vex, devise**) them.

5. In spite of my (**barter, trepidation**) about making a speech at the assembly, I found it an enjoyable experience.

6. I wouldn't describe our hostess as merely (**personable, dexterous**); I think she is a truly captivating woman.

7. Despite my best efforts, I was unable to (**habituate, ferret**) out the time and place of the meeting.

8. My cousin is full of (**personable, whimsical**) ideas that may not be practical but are a lot of fun to discuss.

9. My ingenious sister (**vexed, devised**) a gadget that opens cans, secures nails, and loosens bolts.

10. Although we all long for world peace, we should not allow ourselves to (**habituate, barter**) away our liberties to secure it.

11. Instead of trying to (**scoff, devise**) an elaborate excuse, why not tell them exactly what happened and hope for the best?

12. As a child, I loved L. M. Montgomery's stories of the (**whimsical, dexterous**) orphan, Anne of Green Gables, who was brimming with fanciful ideas.

Completing the Sentence

Choose the word from the word bank that best completes each of the following sentences. Write the correct word or form of the word in the space provided.

barter	dexterous	habituate	scoff	vex
devise	ferret	personable	trepidation	whimsical

1. Her early years on her family's farm _____ her to long hours and hard manual labor.

2. The purpose of this meeting is to _____ a plan for encouraging recycling in our community.

3. You should try not to allow petty annoyances to _____ you so much.

4. It is the job of a gossip columnist to _____ out the "secrets of the stars."

5. The salesclerk didn't seem to know the stock very well, but he was so pleasant and _____ that we were glad to have him serving us.

6. Although I have read *Peter Pan* many times, the _____ characters and imaginative story never fail to amuse me.

7. When I think of all the things that could go wrong, I view the task ahead with great _____.

8. At a well-known theater in Virginia, playgoers could _____ various kinds of food for the price of admission.

9. The _____ fingers of the great violinist were guided by his deep understanding of the music.

10. Before you make fun of my new automatic back scratcher, remember how people _____ at Edison and the Wright brothers.

Synonyms

*Choose the word or form of the word from this Unit that is the same or most nearly the same in meaning as the **boldface** word or expression in the phrase. Write that word on the line. Use a dictionary if necessary.*

1. **adapted** our lives to the new surroundings   _____

2. the surprising **vigor** of a 90-year-old man   _____

3. **teased** out the information   _____

4. signed an **agreement** for peace   _____

5. **requires** a thorough knowledge of math   _____

6. completely **immersed** in the new book   _____

7. felt **apprehension** about her final exam   _____

8. **distressed** by his insensitive comments   _____

9. the dancer's **agile** movements   _____

10. a **real** mountain of debt   _____

11. **designed** a machine to make dough faster   _____

12. **reprimanded** the cat for stalking the bird   _____

13. **traded** gold coins for spices   _____

14. prepared for the **approaching** deadline   _____

15. the **changeover** to daylight saving time   _____

Antonyms

*Choose the word or form of the word from this Unit that is most nearly opposite in meaning to the **boldface** word or expression in the phrase. Write that word on the line. Use a dictionary if necessary.*

1. **cherish** our long separation   _____

2. an **obnoxious** club member   _____

3. never expected such **courteous** treatment   _____

4. **admire** our hard work   _____

5. a **somber** view of the world   _____

Writing: Words in Action

Suppose that you are one of the explorers who agrees with Cabeza de Vaca that the group should stay together. Write a letter to Narváez to explain the probable effects of dividing the group. Use at least two details from the passage (pages 144–145) and three or more words from this Unit.

Vocabulary in Context

*Some of the words you have studied in this Unit appear in **boldface** type. Read the passage below, and then circle the letter of the correct answer for each word as it is used in context.*

In 1738, more than a century before the Civil War, 100 black men, women, and children founded a new town and fort in Spanish-held Florida, near St. Augustine. The community was established in **accord** with the state's **personable** Spanish governor and the king of Spain. It was given a long, official Spanish name that most would **scoff** at if they heard it, so it was commonly known as Fort Mosé (*Moh-say*). It was the first free black settlement in colonial America.

Fort Mosé's settlers were formerly enslaved but had escaped horrifying conditions at British-owned plantations in the Carolinas, north of Florida. They sought sanctuary in Florida, which had been annexed by Spain in 1513. They soon **habituated** to their new settlement.

It was no **whimsical** plan that brought the refugees to Florida. Spain's assimilation policy gave formerly enslaved people unheard-of freedom and opportunities. It wasn't always peaceful, though. There was plenty of bad blood and fighting among the different factions as each group fought to maintain control. Fort Mosé's inhabitants farmed the land with **vitality** while maintaining a militia to protect St. Augustine, the capital of Spanish Florida.

Many historians view the former slaves' escape route south to Florida as an earlier version of the famous nineteenth-century Underground Railroad. Today, the site of Fort Mosé is on the Florida Black Heritage Trail and is considered an essential part of African American history.

---

1. **Accord** comes from the Latin word **accordare. Accordare** most likely means
   a. to start a petition
   b. to strike a bargain
   c. to bring into agreement
   d. to seek out freedom

2. What is the meaning of **personable** as it is used in paragraph 1?
   a. petty
   b. delusional
   c. agreeable
   d. optimistic

3. What word means the same as **scoff** as it is used in paragraph 1?
   a. ridicule
   b. misunderstand
   c. take part
   d. take offense

4. What does **habituated** most likely mean as it is used in paragraph 2?
   a. escaped from
   b. caused injury
   c. became used to
   d. became valuable

5. The word **whimsical** means about the same as
   a. unpredictable
   b. misguided
   c. original
   d. unacceptable

6. In paragraph 3, what does the use of the word **vitality** suggest about the settlers?
   a. They were resilient.
   b. They kept learning.
   c. They were miserable.
   d. They were poor.

Read the following passage, taking note of the **boldface** words and their contexts. These words are among those you will be studying in Unit 11. It may help you to complete the exercises in this Unit if you refer to the way the words are used below.

Working Like a Dog

<Interview>

Last month, Working Dog *magazine editor Fran Y. DeSoto sat down with dog trainer I. Lee Hsu to find out more about service dogs and therapy dogs.*

Interviewer: I. Lee Hsu, you're an animal trainer who works with service dogs and therapy dogs. What is the difference?

Hsu: If you **delve** into it, there are many differences. The **conventional** view is that service dogs are guide dogs for the blind or the hearing impaired, and while that's true, they are also trained to pull wheelchairs, be alert to the sounds of a telephone ringing or a smoke detector beeping, and even retrieve keys or call 911. Service dogs are picked for specific characteristics and temperament. They are not

Therapy dogs lift the spirits of battle-scarred soldiers.

pets; they are working dogs. But that's not to say that a strong, loving partnership doesn't develop between the dog and the person. The intelligence, kindness, and **gallantry** of these dogs can't be underestimated.

Therapy dogs provide comfort and healing to their owners or to people in hospitals, retirement homes, rehabilitation facilities, or any therapeutic setting. The dogs are brought into a **milieu** where someone needs TLC—tender, loving care—and they are just about the best stress busters around! Therapy dogs are usually pets and don't have the same rigorous training as the service dogs, though they must be well-behaved.

Interviewer: Which breeds make better service dogs or therapy dogs?

Hsu: Labradors and golden retrievers are the most popular choice for service dogs. I'll **cite** a few reasons: They are smart, obedient, confident, hardworking, and highly trainable. Dogs that are too distractible, exuberant, or shy don't make the cut. Therapy dogs come in all types and sizes and can be any breed, as long as they are friendly and respond well to touch and lots of handling.

Interviewer: How does a dog become a service dog?

Hsu: I work with an organization that breeds and trains service dogs, and then matches them with people. The dogs live with a foster family for the first year to socialize them and get them used to being around all types of people and situations. Then a period of intensive training **ensues** before the dogs are paired with a human partner.

Interviewer: How do therapy dogs help people?

Hsu: I could **regale** you with heartwarming stories of therapy dogs brought into hospitals to visit sick children or into a home for the elderly or disabled. The dogs are there to be themselves

Therapy dogs offer love and companionship to senior citizens.

Interviewer: What is a trainer's role?

Hsu: Trainers **impart** their knowledge and experience to both dog and prospective owner. Like humans, dogs have unique traits and **quirks**, and some can be **overbearing** towards other dogs—so we weed out dogs that might cause problems. I have had to **mediate** a few minor scuffles, but nothing too crazy or **outlandish**.

Interviewer: What's your favorite part of the job?

Hsu: It's gratifying to see the young service dogs chow down after a long day of training. There's **judicious** use of rewards, and they have their playtime, too—it's not all work. And it's satisfying to see the positive difference these dogs make in people's lives.

and allow people to pet them. They calm and soothe, lower blood pressure, boost health, and provide much-needed affection. They have proven invaluable in **appeasing** kids who have suffered a traumatic event or soldiers who have sustained a **calamitous** injury.

Audio

For iWords and audio passages, go to SadlierConnect.com.

Service dogs are trained to be in working mode when the vest is on.

Definitions

Note the spelling, pronunciation, part(s) of speech, and definition(s) of each of the following words. Then write the appropriate form of the word in the blank space in the illustrative sentence(s) following.

1. **belated**
   (bi lā' tid)

   (*adj.*) late, tardy

   The _____ arrival of the party's guest of honor put the hosts in an awkward position.

2. **cite**
   (sīt)

   (*v.*) to quote; to mention; to summon to appear in court; to commend, recommend

   Be sure to _____ your sources when you write a research paper.

3. **conventional**
   (kən ven' shə nəl)

   (*adj.*) in line with accepted ideas or standards; trite

   Many people have _____ taste in clothing.

4. **decoy**
   (*v.*, di koi';
   n., dē' koi)

   (*v.*) to lure into a trap; (*n.*) a person or thing used to lure into a trap

   The Pied Piper _____ all the children away from the town of Hamelin by playing his flute.

   Painted wooden _____ are prized by collectors of folk art as well as by hunters.

5. **ensue**
   (en sü')

   (*v.*) to follow in order, come immediately after, and as a result

   When an airplane crashes, both investigations and lawsuits can be expected to _____.

6. **mediate**
   (*v.*, mē' dē āt;
   adj., mē' dē ət)

   (*v.*) to bring about an agreement between persons or groups, act as a go-between; (*adj.*) occupying a middle position; indirect, acting through an intermediary

   A neutral third party often _____ contract talks between labor and management.

   The name of the _____ star in Orion's Belt is Alnilam.

7. **milieu**
   (mēl yü')

   (*n.*) the setting, surroundings, environment

   An authentic _____ is an essential ingredient in a good historical novel.

8. outlandish
(aút land' ish)

(*adj.*) strange, freakish, weird, foreign-looking; out-of-the-way, geographically remote; exceeding reasonable limits

Imaginative and _____ outfits are popular attire at a costume party.

9. pert
(pərt)

(*adj.*) high-spirited; lively; bold, saucy; jaunty

Most adults are willing to tolerate a certain amount of _____ behavior in children.

10. taint
(tānt)

(*n.*) a stain or spot; a mark of corruption or dishonor; (*v.*) to stain or contaminate

The _____ of bribery can put an end to the career of a public official.

When toxic chemicals _____ lakes and rivers, many fish and other animals die.

Using Context

*For each item, determine whether the **boldface** word from pages 158–159 makes sense in the context of the sentence. Circle the item numbers next to the six sentences in which the words are used correctly.*

1. Tall tales focus on larger-than-life characters and their **outlandish** adventures.

2. Emily Dickinson lived a quiet and outwardly **conventional** life in Amherst, Massachusetts, while writing startlingly fresh and experimental poetry in private.

3. Since 1886, the Statue of Liberty has stood as a **decoy** of freedom in New York Harbor.

4. A **belated** apology for an insensitive remark is better than no apology at all.

5. Serious sports fans can **cite** an impressive variety of statistics about their favorite teams.

6. If you do not properly brush and floss your teeth, dental problems are likely to **ensue.**

7. Critics who reviewed the movie were careful not to give away the shocking **milieu** at the end.

8. The crocodile is a **pert** hunter that can wait for hours and then suddenly ambush its prey.

9. The rumors of cheating were never proven, but they continue to **taint** the image of the second-place finisher.

10. Long before the existence of modern technology, Polynesians were able to **mediate** by the stars and cross the vast Pacific Ocean.

Choosing the Right Word

*Select the **boldface** word that better completes each sentence. You might refer to the passage on pages 156–157 to see how most of these words are used in context. Note that the choices might be related forms of the Unit words.*

1. One of the chief functions of the United Nations is to (**ensue, mediate**) disputes between member nations.

2. Although some may dismiss "rags-to-riches" stories as silly, I can (**cite, taint**) many examples of wealthy, powerful people who had humble beginnings.

3. When he finally made (**belated, outlandish**) repayment of the money he owed me, he acted as though he was doing me a big favor.

4. Language that seems appropriate in the (**milieu, taint**) of the locker room may be totally out of place in the classroom.

5. Helen's physical appearance does not make her stand out, but her high spirits and (**conventional, pert**) demeanor make her captivating and appealing.

6. I am taking this step with my eyes open, and I will accept full responsibility for whatever may (**ensue, mediate**).

7. Although Marge forgot her sister's birthday, she did manage to send her a (**tainted, belated**) birthday card.

8. If you believe a story as (**outlandish, conventional**) as that, I think you would believe anything!

9. Do you know the proper way to (**cite, ensue**) a source from the Internet?

10. Instead of relying on a (**belated, conventional**) textbook, our social studies teacher uses many different materials and media in the classroom.

11. Though Benedict Arnold originally fought for the American cause, his name is forever (**ensued, tainted**) by his ultimate act of treachery.

12. We will not allow ourselves to be (**decoyed, cited**) into supporting candidates who try to mislead the voters.

Completing the Sentence

Choose the word from the word bank that best completes each of the following sentences. Write the correct word or form of the word in the space provided.

belated	conventional	ensue	milieu	pert
cite	decoy	mediate	outlandish	taint

1. "In that smart new outfit, you look as _____ and stylish as a model," I said to my sister.

2. I don't like listening to my older sisters quarrel, so I sometimes step in and attempt to _____ their disagreements.

3. After seven owners had made additions to the house, each in a different style, the building looked so _____ that no one would buy it.

4. When the American people learned of the bombing of Pearl Harbor in December 1941, they realized that war must _____.

5. Although I know I should have written long before now, I hope you will accept my _____ thanks for the beautiful gift you sent.

6. After many years of public service, she has a splendid record without the slightest _____ of wrongdoing.

7. We all know that our coach is strict, but can you _____ a single instance in which he has been unfair?

8. Some people will never do the _____ thing when it is possible to behave in an unusual or shocking way.

9. Two of the youngsters acted as _____ while a third tried to swipe a few apples from the unguarded bin.

10. Having grown up in a(n) _____ where children were "seen and not heard," my grandfather is perplexed by the outspoken behavior of today's youth.

Definitions

Note the spelling, pronunciation, part(s) of speech, and definition(s) of each of the following words. Then write the appropriate form of the word in the blank space in the illustrative sentence(s) following.

1. appease
(ə pēz')

(*v.*) to make calm, soothe; to relieve, satisfy; to yield to
A snack of fresh fruit should _____ your hunger until mealtime.

2. calamitous
(kə lam' it əs)

(*adj.*) causing great misfortune
In 1906, a _____ earthquake and fire leveled much of the city of San Francisco.

3. delve
(delv)

(*v.*) to dig; to search deeply and thoroughly into
Scholars continue to _____ into all aspects of America's Civil War.

4. gallantry
(gal' ən trē)

(*n.*) heroic courage; respect and courtesy; an act or statement marked by a high level of courtesy
The Medal of Honor is awarded by Congress to those who perform acts of "conspicuous _____" in combat.

5. impart
(im pärt')

(*v.*) to make known, tell; to give, pass something on
All over the world, elders _____ the traditions of their culture to younger generations.

6. judicious
(jü dish' əs)

(*adj.*) using or showing good judgment, wise, sensible
Cautious and _____ people consider all their options before making important decisions.

7. overbearing
(ō vər bâr' iŋ)

(*adj.*) domineering, haughty, bullying; overpowering, predominant
An _____ person has a strong need to be in charge all the time.

8. quirk
(kwərk)

(*n.*) a peculiar way of acting; a sudden twist or turn
A writer may be famous for creating characters who are full of interesting _____.

9. regale
(ri gāl')

(*v.*) to feast, entertain agreeably

Most people are eager to _____ their friends with accounts of their vacation adventures.

10. shiftless
(shift' ləs)

(*adj.*) lazy, lacking in ambition and energy; inefficient

How can anyone lead a _____ life when there are so many interesting things to learn and to see?

Using Context

*For each item, determine whether the **boldface** word from pages 162–163 makes sense in the context of the sentence. Circle the item numbers next to the six sentences in which the words are used correctly.*

1. The exhausted mother could not wait to **regale** to her bed after a long day taking care of the kids.

2. The witness reacted with such **gallantry** when asked why he had been at the scene of the crime that the investigators began to suspect him of the wrongdoing.

3. The restaurant manager tried to **appease** the enraged customer with a free meal, but even that did not seem to diminish his anger.

4. The trainee begged the more seasoned employees to **impart** to her their knowledge on how to succeed at the company.

5. Her **judicious** decision to move across the country, where she has no friends or family, seems reckless to us but she is excited for an adventure.

6. Rather than becoming **shiftless** and uninspired, her experiences of failure have only served to encourage her to succeed even more.

7. Though I was not too excited about my research project when I began, the information I found was so fascinating that I could not help but **delve** into every new detail I came across.

8. I want a mentor that will guide me in what to do, but not one so **overbearing** that I will never be encouraged to think for myself.

9. I found myself in a **calamitous** situation when I could not decide between going away to camp or working during the summer.

10. I am so familiar with my friend's every **quirk** that I don't even realize the behavior others might find odd.

Choosing the Right Word

*Select the **boldface** word that better completes each sentence. You might refer to the passage on pages 156–157 to see how most of these words are used in context. Note that the choices might be related forms of the Unit words.*

1. Foolishly, Neville Chamberlain attempted to avoid a second world war by (**regaling, appeasing**) Hitler's demands for territory in Europe.

2. In debate she has the (**overbearing, shiftless**) manner of one who believes firmly that she is never wrong.

3. Shawn has the most annoying (**quirk, gallantry**); he cracks his knuckles loudly just before he turns on his computer.

4. By careful planning and (**overbearing, judicious**) investments, Sue greatly increased the fortune that her parents had left her.

5. The company has called in an efficiency expert to increase productivity and root out (**judicious, shiftless**) work habits.

6. Whatever his later failures, let us remember that he won the nation's highest military decoration for (**gallantry, quirks**) in action.

7. Our neighbor came over to (**regale, delve**) us with all the gossip that we had missed during our trip.

8. As every baseball player knows, a knuckleball is extremely hard to hit because its flight is full of unexpected (**quirks, gallantry**) called *breaks*.

9. Trying to (**regale, appease**) her best friend, Maya agreed to dine at a pizzeria when she really wanted to eat at the new Chinese restaurant.

10. The best way to (**appease, impart**) a spirit of patriotism to young people is to teach them about the ideals on which this nation is built.

11. Though some people believe we should make more use of nuclear power, others insist that such a decision would be (**shiftless, calamitous**).

12. The more I (**regale, delve**) into mythology, the more clearly I see how these ancient stories help us understand the basic truths of life.

Completing the Sentence

Choose the word from the word bank that best completes each of the following sentences. Write the correct word or form of the word in the space provided.

appease	delve	impart	overbearing	regale
calamitous	gallantry	judicious	quirk	shiftless

1. His devil-may-care attitude toward his job eventually earned him a reputation for being _____ and unreliable.

2. In spite of all that has been reported about pollution, some people still do not grasp its _____ effects on the environment.

3. A good teacher can give you knowledge and skills but cannot _____ the wisdom that comes only with experience.

4. After our bitter quarrel, my brother tried to _____ me by offering to lend me his bicycle.

5. He _____ us with food, drink, and endless stories of his seafaring days.

6. When we were upset and confused, it was only your _____ advice that prevented us from doing something foolish.

7. Giving up your bus seat to a pretty girl is showing off, but giving it up to a tired senior citizen is true _____.

8. A good supervisor is one who can be firm and efficient without giving the impression of being _____.

9. As my friend became older, the _____ in his behavior grew stranger and more difficult to deal with.

10. Without trying to _____ deeply into the reasons for their conduct, just briefly describe what they did.

Synonyms

*Choose the word or form of the word from this Unit that is the same or most nearly the same in meaning as the **boldface** word or expression in the phrase. Write that word on the line. Use a dictionary if necessary.*

1. created a **diversion** to catch the thieves   _____
2. **amused** us with jokes and silly antics   _____
3. a memorable show of **valor**   _____
4. **pacify** the crying baby   _____
5. **burrowed** deeply in the bag for a pencil   _____
6. has many endearing **eccentricities**   _____
7. looked to her mentor for **prudent** advice   _____
8. a **domineering** boss   _____
9. used **commonplace** symbols to communicate   _____
10. thunderous clapping **followed**   _____
11. **convey** news about the candidates' campaigns   _____
12. the **catastrophic** fall of stock prices   _____
13. cannot explain such **peculiar** behavior   _____
14. tried to **settle** arguments between neighbors   _____
15. raised in a loving **environment**   _____

Antonyms

*Choose the word or form of the word from this Unit that is most nearly opposite in meaning to the **boldface** word or expression in the phrase. Write that word on the line. Use a dictionary if necessary.*

1. tablets that will **purify** the water   _____
2. thanking you **in advance**   _____
3. possessing a **sullen** personality   _____
4. a group of **hardworking** interns   _____
5. **ignored** the facts   _____

Writing: Words in Action

Do you think that animals should be trained to help people, or does this kind of training go against the animal's nature? Write a brief essay in which you support your opinion with evidence from the reading (pages 156–157) or from your own knowledge or experience. Use three or more words from this Unit.

Vocabulary in Context

*Some of the words you have studied in this Unit appear in **boldface** type. Read the passage below, and then circle the letter of the correct answer for each word as it is used in context.*

Most scientists **cite** the wolf, *Canis lupus,* as the ancestor of today's decidedly more **shiftless** domestic dogs. But on the critical issue of *when* dog domestication took place, there is often **pert**, and sometimes strident, disagreement among experts. New scientific tools, such as DNA analysis, are constantly emerging. They add new information that sometimes confuses, rather than clarifies, an already confusing area of research.

For decades, the agricultural revolution, which developed in western Asia some 10,000 years ago, marked the most likely point for domestication of the dog. However, new evidence found in Siberia's Taymyr Peninsula in the Russian Far North suggests that such a **belated** date is merely a **decoy**. Experts now theorize that dogs could have assumed their position as humans' best friend tens of thousands of years earlier.

It is difficult not to **taint** such research into ancient origins with bias. But the inquiry into dog domestication will inevitably have to deal with skepticism about the nature of any relationship between ancient humans and wolves. How likely was it that human beings "adopted" a competing predator? Or how likely was it that a canine ancestor, the wolf, took the initiative to adopt a human being?

The inference that a hunter-gatherer kidnapped a wolf puppy from its den and began to raise increasingly tamed wolves is unlikely. For one thing, wolves are exceptionally difficult to tame. In the words of one expert, many researchers find it "more plausible that dogs, in effect, invented themselves."

1. **Cite** comes from the Latin word **citare. Citare** most likely means
   a. to dispute
   b. to argue
   c. to proclaim
   d. to quote

2. The word **shiftless** means about the same as
   a. imprudent
   b. lazy
   c. various
   d. nimble

3. What is the meaning of **pert** as it is used in paragraph 1?
   a. angry
   b. sullen
   c. lively
   d. peevish

4. What is the meaning of **belated** as it is used in paragraph 2?
   a. tardy
   b. foolish
   c. odd
   d. shameful

5. Which word means the same as **decoy** as it is used in paragraph 2?
   a. error
   b. joke
   c. illusion
   d. bait

6. What does **taint** most likely mean as it is used in paragraph 3?
   a. describe
   b. tarnish
   c. denounce
   d. report

*Read the following passage, taking note of the **boldface** words and their contexts. These words are among those you will be studying in Unit 12. It may help you to complete the exercises in this Unit if you refer to the way the words are used below.*

To the Bat Cave!
<Informational Essay>

One day in the late 1800s, while riding near New Mexico's Carlsbad Caverns, cowboy Jim White thought he saw smoke plumes rising in the distance. On closer approach, however, he found that this impression was a **fallacy**. What he had really glimpsed was a cloud of bats emerging from the entrance to a **capacious** cave.

The Carlsbad Caverns house thousands of Mexican free-tailed bats.

It was a **pivotal** moment that changed the history of Carlsbad Caverns. For millions of years, this spectacular underground formation was known only to a sprinkling of Paleo-Indians and to a millionfold colony of bats. Now the caverns would be the **recipient** of world-class scientific investigation and the attention of countless tourists.

The subterranean geological wonders of Carlsbad Caverns are impressive, but it is the bats that grab everyone's attention. From April to October, the cavern ceilings **teem** with hundreds of thousands of Mexican free-tailed bats (*Tadarida brasiliensis*). The cave is

The bats of Carlsbad Caverns emerge from their caves each night.

a maternity roost where the bats bear and rear their young. The total darkness of the cave is a refuge for the bats from predators and from people. For centuries, bats have been the victims of countless myths and **caustic** criticism. These false **tenets** are a Pandora's box for these creatures, engendering hatred and fear that has caused humans to mistreat and misunderstand bats for centuries. For people who like bats, a view of thousands upon thousands of bats flying out of the mouth of the cavern for a night of hunting is not to be missed.

Their flight may appear erratic or even **ungainly**. But nature has **bestowed** on bats one of the most sophisticated guidance systems known to science. Mexican freetails, like most bats, use echolocation to navigate and to locate their prey. The bats send out ultrahigh frequency sounds, similar to those emitted by dolphins and whales. When these signals strike an object, their reflections enable the bat to pinpoint the object and fly accordingly. This process occurs in a fraction of a second. Echolocation ensures that practically no **ruse** or evasive action will allow a bat's targeted prey to escape.

A Mexican freetail's **voracious** appetite is one of the bat's prime gifts to humanity. On its nightly flights, one bat may gorge on half its weight in prey. They eat mosquitoes, moths, and other night-flying insects. The bats of Carlsbad Caverns are small. They weigh in at four to five ounces and have a twelve-inch wingspan.

But experts estimate that these diminutive creatures dispose of more than one million pounds of insects annually. Without the bats, the corn and cotton growers in the region would find their agricultural pest problems far less **tractable**. In addition to helping farmers with insect control, bats also provide fertilizer in the form of guano, or droppings. Bat guano was mined for some years after the discovery of the caverns. Mining guano might seem gross or **nauseating**, but it was highly profitable. Guano mining is no longer allowed, as it disturbs the stunning cave environment and the bats.

Nowadays, Carlsbad Caverns is recognized as a unique national treasure. Preservation groups organize **crusades** to maintain the pristine beauty of the caves and to ensure that tourists do not **deface** the rock formations. Meanwhile, the bats inhabit the caves as they have for millennia.

Audio

For iWords and audio passages, go to SadlierConnect.com.

Definitions

Note the spelling, pronunciation, part(s) of speech, and definition(s) of each of the following words. Then write the appropriate form of the word in the blank space in the illustrative sentence(s) following.

1. abdicate
(ab′ də kāt)

(*v.*) to resign, formally give up an office or a duty; to disown, discard

Of all England's monarchs, Edward VIII was the only one to _____ the throne voluntarily.

2. capacious
(kə pā′ shəs)

(*adj.*) able to hold much, roomy

Whenever I go beach-combing, I take along a backpack with _____ compartments and pockets.

3. crusade
(krü sād′)

(*n.*) a strong movement to advance a cause or idea; (*v.*) to campaign, work vigorously

Rachel Carson's landmark book *Silent Spring* sparked the _____ to ban the use of DDT.

The people who _____ for civil rights in America during the 1960s came from all walks of life.

4. deface
(di fās′)

(*v.*) to injure or destroy the surface or appearance of; to damage the value, influence, or effect of; to face down, outshine

In many towns, those who _____ walls with graffiti must pay a fine and clean up the mess.

5. fallacy
(fal′ ə sē)

(*n.*) a false notion or belief; an error in thinking

Reviewers cited several major _____ in the controversial author's newest book.

6. negate
(ni gāt′)

(*v.*) to nullify, deny, bring to nothing

One offensive remark may well _____ the goodwill a politician has built up among voters.

7. pivotal
(piv′ ət əl)

(*adj.*) vitally important, essential

The D-Day invasion was _____ to the Allies' eventual victory in Europe in World War II.

8. recipient
(ri sip′ ē ənt)

(*n.*) one who receives; (*adj.*) receiving; able or willing to receive

The first American _____ of the Nobel Prize in Literature was the novelist Sinclair Lewis.

A long list of _____ charities may benefit from a wealthy individual's generosity.

9. tenet
(ten' ət)

(n.) an opinion, belief, or principle held to be true
One of the primary _____ of medicine is to do no harm to the sick and injured.

10. ungainly
(ən gān' lē)

(adj.) clumsy, awkward; unwieldy
The first time I tried to ice-skate, my movements were hesitant and _____.

Using Context

*For each item, determine whether the **boldface** word from pages 170–171 makes sense in the context of the sentence. Circle the item numbers next to the six sentences in which the words are used correctly.*

1. Geocentrism, or the notion that Earth is the center of the universe, is an example of a famous historical **fallacy**.

2. The arts committee's **tenet** is to raise at least as much money this year as it did last year.

3. The police officers and detectives will immediately **abdicate** the crime scene so that they can collect evidence.

4. The passengers were pleasantly surprised to discover that the cabins on the cruise ship were both comfortable and **capacious**.

5. The deputy mayor is expected to **deface** all accusations of corruption in the press conference that will take place later today.

6. The bombing of Pearl Harbor on December 7, 1941, was a **pivotal** event; the next day, the United States declared war on Japan.

7. Painting the wooden floor might **negate** the damage that has resulted from years of wear and tear, but it will not repair that damage.

8. The package could not be delivered because the signature of the **recipient** was required, and no one was at the address to accept it.

9. Large birds such as geese often seem **ungainly** when they walk on land, but, by contrast, they are powerful and graceful when they are in flight.

10. Thanks to a successful **crusade** by both citizens and public officials, the city will adopt a zero-waste policy—meaning that all trash will be recycled rather than sent to incinerators or landfills.

Choosing the Right Word

*Select the **boldface** word that better completes each sentence. You might refer to the passage on pages 168–169 to see how most of these words are used in context. Note that the choices might be related forms of the Unit words.*

1. Although the play is titled *Julius Caesar,* I think that the (**pivotal, capacious**) character, on whom all the action depends, is Mark Antony.

2. Instead of launching a great (**crusade, fallacy**) to save the world, why not try to help a few people in your own neighborhood?

3. We will not allow you to (**negate, abdicate**) your responsibilities as a leading citizen of this community.

4. One guiding (**tenet, crusade**) of our energy program is that it is just as important to avoid wasting energy as it is to increase its production.

5. The fact that she is not a member of the Board of Education does not (**negate, abdicate**) her criticisms of the school system.

6. It is a (**fallacy, tenet**) to say that because no human being has ever traveled to Mars, no human being ever will.

7. The tall boy who appeared so (**capacious, ungainly**) as he walked through the school corridors was agile and coordinated on the basketball court.

8. Weather and pollution had so (**defaced, abdicated**) the statue that its original expression was no longer distinguishable.

9. The Slam-Dunk Giveaway will send one lucky (**recipient, tenet**) on a paid vacation for two to lovely Hawaii.

10. She has a (**capacious, pivotal**) mind that seems able to hold endless information and ideas on any subject.

11. One of the (**tenets, fallacies**) of modern art is to experiment with forms, materials, and processes to create new ways of looking at everyday objects.

12. When the United States gives out foreign aid, are the (**recipient, pivotal**) nations supposed to make repayment?

Completing the Sentence

Choose the word from the word bank that best completes each of the following sentences. Write the correct word or form of the word in the space provided.

abdicate	crusade	fallacy	pivotal	tenet
capacious	deface	negate	recipient	ungainly

1. In the early decades of the twentieth century, reform-minded journalists called *muckrakers* _____ vigorously against corruption in government.

2. It was not hard for Ted's opponents to shoot holes in his argument, since the _____ it contained were as clear as day.

3. Although seals and sea lions are _____ on land, they are extremely graceful in the water.

4. Though a number of people may be nominated for the Best Actress Oscar each year, only one of them will be the actual _____ of it.

5. For thousands of years, thoughtless tourists have _____ monuments of the past by writing or carving their initials on them.

6. A fundamental _____ of democracy is that all people are equal before the law.

7. Dad said that he was enjoying the fig-banana pie I had concocted, but the funny look on his face _____ his words.

8. Our victory over South High was the _____ game of the season because it gave us the self-confidence we needed to win the championship.

9. I have never seen a car with a trunk _____ enough to hold all the luggage you want to take on any trip.

10. When he realized that he had completely lost the loyalty and support of his people, the ruler of the small nation chose to _____ and live in exile.

Definitions

Note the spelling, pronunciation, part(s) of speech, and definition(s) of each of the following words. Then write the appropriate form of the word in the blank space in the illustrative sentence(s) following.

1. bestow
(bi stō′)

(*v.*) to give as a gift; to provide with lodgings
The nation will _____ its highest civilian honor on the noted educator.

2. caustic
(kô′ stik)

(*adj.*) able to burn or eat away by chemical action; biting, sarcastic
All _____ household liquids, such as drain cleaners, must be kept out of the reach of children.

3. embargo
(em bär′ gō)

(*n.*) an order forbidding the trade in or movement of commercial goods; any restraint or hindrance;
(*v.*) to forbid to enter or leave port; to forbid trade with

The U.S. Congress may impose an _____ against a country that violates trade agreements.
In wartime, the President may _____ goods from countries that trade with the nation's foes.

4. levity
(lev′ ə tē)

(*n.*) a lack of seriousness or earnestness, especially about things that should be treated with respect; buoyancy, lightness in weight
A bit of _____ may help you to cope with difficult people or situations.

5. mendicant
(men′ də kənt)

(*n.*) beggar; (*adj.*) depending on begging for a living
People who have fallen on hard times may have no choice but to become _____.
_____ friars roamed the streets of medieval towns and cities, asking for coins.

6. nauseate
(nô′ zē āt)

(*v.*) to make sick to the stomach; to fill with disgust
The fumes that _____ everyone in the building were traced to a faulty heating system.

7. ruse
(rüz)

(*n.*) an action designed to confuse or mislead, a trick
Thieves employ a variety of _____ to gain entrance to homes and apartments.

8. teem
(tēm)

(*v.*) to become filled to overflowing; to be present in large quantities
State parks _____ with summer visitors.

9. tractable
(trak′ tə bəl)

(*adj.*) easily managed, easy to deal with; easily wrought, malleable

A _____ colleague is preferable to one who is unwilling to cooperate or compromise.

10. voracious
(vô rā′ shəs)

(*adj.*) having a huge appetite, greedy, ravenous; excessively eager

Newly hatched caterpillars are _____ eaters of leafy green plants.

Using Context

*For each item, determine whether the **boldface** word from pages 174–175 makes sense in the context of the sentence. Circle the item numbers next to the six sentences in which the words are used correctly.*

1. If the sight of blood is enough to **nauseate** you, then you might want to reconsider your goal of becoming a doctor.

2. The volunteer was described as a **mendicant** who always prioritized others before herself.

3. The university plans to **bestow** an honorary degree on the accomplished guest speaker.

4. The security guard was not fooled by the **ruse** often used by shoplifters of pulling the fire alarm in order to distract the employees.

5. She is such a **voracious** learner that it seems she'll never be able to find enough information on any given subject to satisfy her.

6. Since my brother and I constantly bicker, my mother put an **embargo** on any fighting during the family reunion.

7. Although I intended to stay inside and study all day, I could not let the last **caustic** day of summer go to waste, so I headed to the park to do my reading outside.

8. The color seemed to **teem** from her face when she heard news of the recent tragedy.

9. He has a good sense of humor, but it was wrong to speak of the tragedy with such **levity**.

10. We were all moved by the **tractable** story of the lost dog finding his way home.

Choosing the Right Word

*Select the **boldface** word that better completes each sentence. You might refer to the passage on pages 168–169 to see how most of these words are used in context. Note that the choices might be related forms of the Unit words.*

1. With such a (**tractable, voracious**) appetite, the meat-eating dinosaur T. Rex was a horrifying hunter and scavenger.

2. The four-foot waves made the boat pitch up and down, causing many passengers to become (**caustic, nauseated**).

3. As soon as the new highway extension was built, the sleepy town began to (**teem, bestow**) with activity.

4. Has anyone ever measured how many hours of TV time are needed to satisfy a small child's (**tractable, voracious**) appetite for cartoons?

5. Although the students made jokes about the coming exams, we knew that beneath the (**ruse, levity**) they were quite worried.

6. A favorite bedtime (**mendicant, ruse**) of small children is to keep asking for a glass of water to delay having to go to sleep.

7. It's good to be open to new ideas, but don't become so (**mendicant, tractable**) that you have no firm opinions of your own.

8. His mind is closed, as though he had placed a(n) (**embargo, levity**) on new ideas.

9. I can forgive most human weaknesses, but I am (**nauseated, bestowed**) by hypocrisy.

10. I am willing to become a veritable (**ruse, mendicant**) in order to raise money for that most worthy cause.

11. "All that I have to (**teem, bestow**) on you," said the elderly father to his son, "is an honorable family name."

12. She is a very severe critic, and the (**tractable, caustic**) comments in her reviews have made her many enemies.

Completing the Sentence

Choose the word from the word bank that best completes each of the following sentences. Write the correct word or form of the word in the space provided.

bestow	**embargo**	**mendicant**	**ruse**	**tractable**
caustic	**levity**	**nauseate**	**teem**	**voracious**

1. Whenever I pass a group of homeless _____ huddled in a doorway, I give them my spare change.

2. Since the Greeks could not capture Troy by force, they resorted to the now-legendary _____ of the wooden horse to take the city.

3. Your attempts at _____ during the most serious moments of the dedication ceremony were decidedly out of place.

4. I suspect that they visit the wealthy widow at the nursing home mainly because they think she will _____ part of her fortune on them in gratitude.

5. San Francisco is a city that _____ with color and places of historical interest.

6. The noise in the crowded train station gave me a headache, and the foul odor _____ me.

7. The horse was often hard to manage, but he was _____ as long as he was headed in the direction of the barn.

8. If any of the _____ substance gets on your clothing, wash it off with lukewarm water to prevent it from eating away the fabric.

9. He is such a(n) _____ reader that he often has a book propped up in front of him while he is eating.

10. The President placed a(n) _____ on the sale of arms to the two nations at war.

Synonyms

*Choose the word or form of the word from this Unit that is the same or most nearly the same in meaning as the **boldface** word or expression in the phrase. Write that word on the line. Use a dictionary if necessary.*

1. the **battle** to end poverty   _____

2. set up a **scam** to fool the burglars   _____

3. the **beneficiary** of the scholarship   _____

4. **conferred** on him the rank of knighthood   _____

5. the main **doctrines** of Buddhism   _____

6. **avid** viewers of cable news   _____

7. a theory based entirely on **misconceptions**   _____

8. a dog that is big and **graceless** yet so lovable   _____

9. the leader's **docile** followers   _____

10. a king who was forced to **step down**   _____

11. **bans** on counterfeit designer products   _____

12. a lake **filled** with trout   _____

13. a group of ragged **paupers**   _____

14. possesses a **cutting** wit   _____

15. acts of cruelty that **repulsed** us all   _____

Antonyms

*Choose the word or form of the word from this Unit that is most nearly opposite in meaning to the **boldface** word or expression in the phrase. Write that word on the line. Use a dictionary if necessary.*

1. patiently **confirmed** his remarks   _____

2. a house with **cramped** closets   _____

3. an **insignificant** change to the schedule   _____

4. surprised to see the **restored** painting   _____

5. amused by the **seriousness** of your remarks   _____

Writing: Words in Action

Suppose you are a magazine writer in the early 1900s, when Carlsbad Caverns became a national monument. Write an article persuading readers that the caves are a "geological wonder" and the nightly bat flights should not be missed. Use details from the passage (pages 168–169) and three or more words from this Unit.

Vocabulary in Context

*Some of the words you have studied in this Unit appear in **boldface** type. Read the passage below, and then circle the letter of the correct answer for each word as it is used in context.*

Caves are mysterious spaces created over many hundreds of years by geological processes such as crashing waves, trickling rainwater, flowing lava, or microorganisms like bacteria. A solutional cave is the most common type of cave. It is formed by natural acids in groundwater that dissolve limestone and other rock. Caves are often part of a network of connected passageways and corridors.

Icicle-shaped stalactites, which hang downward from cave ceilings, and rounder-shaped stalagmites, which grow upward from cave floors, are made of mineral deposits left by dripping water. These mineral formations eventually join to form one large natural structure. But here is a bit of **levity** and some free advice: Don't wait around. They grow about one inch every 100 years!

Famous caves such as Mammoth Cave in Kentucky, believed to be the world's longest cave system, often **teem** with cavers and tourists. That's why National Park Service officials have imposed an **embargo** on most visitors to Lechuguilla Cave in New Mexico. They want to **negate** the damage humans can cause. Stunning Lechuguilla, deep underground beneath the Guadalupe Mountains, is limited to approved scientific researchers and survey teams.

Caves have been used since the time of the earliest humans for shelter or as burial sites. History is full of stories of **mendicants** using caves as living quarters when they had nowhere else to go, or of hermits seeking to **abdicate** responsibility and escape the demands of society. Remarkable ancient cave paintings and other treasures have been found in caves all over the world.

---

1. **Levity** comes from the Latin word **levis**. **Levis** most likely means
   a. interest
   b. light
   c. experience
   d. research

2. What does **teem** most likely mean as it is used in paragraph 3?
   a. compare
   b. live
   c. overflow
   d. revolve

3. What is the meaning of **embargo** as it is used in paragraph 3?
   a. identity
   b. ban
   c. permit
   d. label

4. The word **negate** means about the same as
   a. nullify
   b. record
   c. measure
   d. observe

5. What is the meaning of **mendicants** as it is used in paragraph 4?
   a. historians
   b. healers
   c. beggars
   d. travelers

6. Which word means the same as **abdicate** as it is used in paragraph 4?
   a. translate
   b. adopt
   c. recognize
   d. renounce

Vocabulary for Comprehension
Part 1

Read "Kabuki: An Enduring Art Form," which contains words in **boldface** *that appear in Units 10–12. Then answer the questions.*

Kabuki: An Enduring Art Form

About 400 years ago, a spectacular type of theater developed in the ancient Japanese capital city of Kyoto. It is called *Kabuki*, from the words *ka*, which means

(5) "song"; *bu*, which means "dance"; and *ki*, which means "skill." Kabuki actors must excel in all these arts. They undergo many years of rigorous training that usually begins when they are small children.

(10) Over the centuries, Kabuki has developed into a highly stylized art form that **regales** audiences with an exciting blend of song, dance, speech, and mime. With its gorgeous costumes and

(15) spectacular stage effects, Kabuki is a **veritable** feast for the eyes and ears. The inventor of Kabuki was a shrine attendant named Okuni. She began by performing her plays, which were based on Buddhist

(20) themes, in Kyoto's dry riverbeds. Okuni recruited other women performers, and their dance plays quickly became very popular. However, the government considered it improper for women to take

(25) part in theatrical performances. In 1629, it banned women from the stage. Since then, the performers in Kabuki have all been men.

Kabuki was the first Japanese theater

(30) art that was designed to appeal to the common people, rather than the royal court or the warrior class (the samurai). As the merchant class and farmers grew more prosperous during the seventeenth

(35) century, the popularity of Kabuki increased.

The plays performed by Kabuki troupes include historical sagas, love stories, ghost stories, and tales of domestic tragedy. Comic interludes that portray the foolish

(40) **quirks** of human nature are interspersed to add a note of **levity** to the program. And while the plays are intended to entertain, they also **impart** moral lessons, especially that the virtuous are rewarded, and the

(45) wicked are punished.

Perhaps one of the most recognizable features of this traditional form of Japanese theater is the dramatic makeup that its performers often wear. Instead of a

(50) mask, actors usually wear a heavy white foundation that may be accented with stripes and patterns painted in bold colors. Colors and patterns on the actors' faces reveal the types of characters they are

(55) portraying. For example, actors who are playing powerful, heroic characters may have bright red stripes along their cheekbones, jaws, and eyes. Blue markings on the face are generally associated with

(60) ghosts and supernatural characters.

Wearing elaborate makeup, costumes, and wigs, and engaging in highly stylized singing and dancing, Kabuki performers transform into almost-otherworldly entities

(65) on stage. Though Kabuki is hundreds of years old, it is not a dusty relic. It retains tremendous **vitality** and continues to delight audiences wherever it is performed.

1. Based on the evidence in the passage, what is **most likely** the author's purpose in "Kabuki: An Enduring Art Form"?
   A) to give a brief biography of Okuni
   B) to explain the cultural history of Japan
   C) to give a brief history of Kabuki
   D) to describe the author's experiences of Kabuki

2. Which statement **best** provides an inference that is supported by lines 4–6?
   A) Kabuki is a type of theater mainly for children.
   B) Kabuki is an art form based in music and dance.
   C) Kabuki originated in ancient Greek drama.
   D) Amateur actors perform Kabuki.

3. What is the meaning of **regales** as it is used in line 12?
   A) entertains
   B) annoys
   C) pacifies
   D) instructs

4. What does the phrase "veritable feast for the eyes and ears" in line 16 suggest?
   A) The dramatic effects of Kabuki are doubtful.
   B) Kabuki has a true ability to entertain audiences.
   C) Kabuki's dramatic effects are meager.
   D) Kabuki is mildly entertaining.

5. Based on the evidence in the passage, which statement **best** explains why all Kabuki performers are men?
   A) Kabuki performances require brute strength.
   B) Kabuki scripts call for male actors only.
   C) Kabuki was originally based on Buddhist themes.
   D) The Japanese government banned women from the stage.

6. **Part A**
   Which word **best** describes the tone of this passage?
   A) ironic
   B) admiring
   C) critical
   D) analytical

   Part B
   Which detail from the passage **best** supports your answer to Part A?
   A) "ancient Japanese capital city of Kyoto" (lines 2–3)
   B) "its gorgeous costumes and spectacular stage effects" (lines 14–15)
   C) "improper for women" (line 24)
   D) "designed to appeal to the common people" (lines 30–31)

7. What does the word **quirks** most likely mean as it is used in line 40?
   A) fantasies
   B) oddities
   C) mistakes
   D) faults

8. What is the meaning of **levity** as it is used in line 41?
   A) pity
   B) sanity
   C) frivolity
   D) solemnity

9. What does the word **impart** most likely mean as it is used in line 43?
   A) ignore
   B) repeat
   C) conceal
   D) transmit

10. Which word means the opposite of **vitality** in line 67?
    A) liveliness
    B) endurance
    C) lifelessness
    D) vigor

Vocabulary for Comprehension
Part 2

*Read these passages, which contain words in **boldface** that appear in Units 10–12. Then choose the best answer to each question based on what is stated or implied in the passage(s). You may refer to the passages as often as necessary.*

Questions 1–10 are based on the following passages.

Passage 1

In a synchrotron, subatomic particles are accelerated to speeds verging on the speed of light. The basic design of this research tool were **devised** at roughly

(5) the same time (1944–1945) by physicists Vladimir Veksler in Russia and Edwin McMillan in the United States.

Over the decades since the synchrotron's development, a host of applications to

(10) research scientists has **ensued**. In the accelerator, the particles' path is altered to produce X-rays that can be focused into an ultra-thin beam. Scientists can use the beam to **ferret** out the details of molecular

(15) structures and to form images of them. The use of synchrotrons is time-consuming and extremely expensive. Nevertheless, the drug and electronic industries see the new technology **teeming** with possibilities, and

(20) have shown a **voracious** appetite for the new data that synchrotrons can produce.

Occasionally, synchrotrons make the headlines in less esoteric arenas. The device has played a key role in preserving

(25) the *Mary Rose*, flagship of King Henry VIII, which sank off England's southern coast in 1545. Half the ship's hull was preserved by silts on the sea bed. To prevent deterioration of the hull from oxygen

(30) exposure now that the ship is out of the water, conservators used a synchrotron to determine precise levels of sulphur and iron in the drying wood.

Passage 2

On August 24, 79 CE, the eruption of

(35) Mount Vesuvius buried the city of Pompeii and its people—rich man and **mendicant** alike—under a flow of lava. Also buried was the smaller town of Herculaneum, an upscale vacation retreat for wealthy Roman

(40) citizens. Ninety feet deep in Pompeii's rubble lay the splendid Villa dei Papiri, a mansion supposedly built by the father-in-law of Julius Caesar. At the heart of this villa was its extensive library, where, in 1752,

(45) archaeologists discovered more than 800 papyrus scrolls. The only problem was how researchers might be able to read them. To unroll the scrolls in their current ultra-fragile condition would be to destroy them.

(50) Enter the synchrotron. In this device, powerful X-rays can be focused into a beam with the width of a strand of hair. The ancient scribes writing on the papyrus had used iron in their ink. Synchrotron-

(55) generated beams could be programmed to look for extremely small concentrations of iron. Despite considerable obstacles of time and expense, researchers now had a potent tool to **delve** into the secrets of

(60) these and other ancient written works.

The synchrotron has also **mediated** far more ancient time gaps. In one **pivotal** research effort, for example, Thomas Van de Kamp and his colleagues showed that

(65) synchrotron-based X-ray microtomography could **bestow** a veritable trove of data about wasps fossilized in amber millions of years ago.

1. According to Passage 1, what does a synchrotron do?
   A) bombards subatomic particles
   B) integrates molecules
   C) accelerates subatomic particles
   D) splits atomic particles

2. As it is used in line 10, "ensued" most nearly means
   A) reduced.
   B) followed.
   C) increased.
   D) verified.

3. From details in Passage 2, it can reasonably be inferred that the father-in-law of Julius Caesar was
   A) wealthy.
   B) aristocratic.
   C) generous.
   D) stingy.

4. As it is used in line 59, "delve" most nearly means
   A) ramble.
   B) steal.
   C) hide.
   D) search.

5. As it is used in line 62, "pivotal" most nearly means
   A) realistic.
   B) circular.
   C) crucial.
   D) insignificant.

6. Passage 1 differs from Passage 2 primarily in that it
   A) mentions several research applications of synchrotrons.
   B) includes more detail about the history and functioning of synchrotrons.
   C) discusses the ever-increasing refinement of synchrotrons.
   D) cites specialized articles written by the early designers of synchrotrons.

7. Which choice provides the best evidence for the answer to the previous question?
   A) Lines 3–7 ("The basic . . . States")
   B) Lines 8–10 ("Over . . . ensued")
   C) Lines 15–17 ("The use . . . expensive")
   D) Lines 22–23 ("Occasionally . . . arenas")

8. Passage 1 and Passage 2 are similar in that both passages stress
   A) the importance of magnetic fields in particle acceleration.
   B) resistance by prominent nuclear physicists to the use of synchrotrons.
   C) the contributions of synchrotrons to the science of earthquake prediction.
   D) the unexpectedly broad range of the applications of synchrotrons.

9. Passage 1 may be contrasted with Passage 2 in that
   A) only Passage 1 includes citation of a news headline.
   B) only Passage 1 refers to the use of the synchrotron by the drug and electronic industries.
   C) the overall organization of Passage 1 is chronological.
   D) Passage 1 stresses cause and effect, while Passage 2 emphasizes comparison and contrast.

10. As it is used in line 66, "bestow" most nearly means
    A) to hide.
    B) to show.
    C) to give.
    D) to take.

Synonyms

*From the word bank below, choose the word that has the same or nearly the same meaning as the **boldface** word in each sentence and write it on the line. You will not use all of the words.*

abdicate	delve	fallacy	regale
accord	engross	ferret	rue
decoy	ensue	habituate	scoff
deface	entail	quirk	upbraid

1. Is the idea that animals can predict earthquakes true, or is it a **misconception**? _____

2. On a rainy weekend, I like to **immerse** myself in a classic detective story. _____

3. A growth on the anglerfish's head looks like a worm and serves as an **attraction** to bring the fish's prey near. _____

4. People who **inure** themselves to staying up late can find it hard to change their sleeping habits. _____

5. The dentist warned me about the kinds of problems that would **result** if I did not floss regularly. _____

6. After just a few weeks, I began to **repent** my decision to sell my guitar and started saving money to buy a new one. _____

7. The conspirators came up with a plot that would force the king to **relinquish** the throne. _____

8. *The Cat in the Hat* always manages to **divert** the preschoolers, no matter how many times they hear the story. _____

9. The actor tried to think of a **peculiarity** that would make the character he was playing distinctive and recognizable. _____

10. The tenants were only able to reach their **mutual understanding** with the new landlord after consulting with a lawyer. _____

11. We are all aware that getting a dog will **necessitate** certain changes in our day-to-day life. _____

12. My environmentally conscious sister tends to **reprimand** me if I leave a room without turning out the lights. _____

Two-Word Completions

Select the pair of words that best completes the meaning of each of the following sentences.

1. "I feel well prepared and don't view the upcoming scholarship examination with any _____," I asserted confidently. "Still, it's a serious matter, and I'm not treating it with undue _____ either."
   a. nausea … dexterity
   b. gallantry … vitality
   c. trepidation … levity
   d. curtness … vexation

2. "That rock group's strange antics, _____ costumes, and weird songs don't really impress me," Clara remarked. "Frankly, I prefer musicians who are much more _____."
   a. bartered … tainted
   b. outlandish … conventional
   c. caustic … whimsical
   d. pert … overbearing

3. The speaker did not _____ many examples to back up her argument, but those that she did provide were extremely well chosen. A larger but less _____ selection of illustrations probably would not have made such a powerful impression on the audience.
   a. impart … outlandish
   b. devise … ungainly
   c. bestow … capacious
   d. cite … judicious

4. Despite the _____ of a few brave men, whose daring deeds on that fateful day are still remembered by history, imperial Rome suffered a(n) _____ defeat that brought a once-mighty empire to its knees.
   a. gallantry … calamitous
   b. trepidation … veritable
   c. dexterity … impending
   d. vitality … whimsical

5. "My ability to hold on to this job will depend on the answer to one _____ question," I thought. "Will I prove to be truly hardworking and reliable, or _____ and irresponsible?"
   a. impending … tractable
   b. caustic … dexterous
   c. whimsical … personable
   d. pivotal … shiftless

6. Long overdue though it surely was, his _____ apology was sufficient to _____ my anger and soothe my hurt feelings.
   a. curt … negate
   b. caustic … mediate
   c. belated … appease
   d. dexterous … vex

7. "Though I'd spent all my life in a rural environment, I didn't think I'd have any trouble adjusting to city life," Ted said to his friend. "But making the _____ to an urban _____ proved to be much more difficult than I had ever imagined."
   a. transition … milieu
   b. ruse … tenet
   c. crusade … recipient
   d. tenet … embargo

Denotation and Connotation

When you are determining the meaning of a word, it's important to consider both its denotation and its connotation. The denotation is the word's definition, its literal meaning as presented in a dictionary. The **denotation** is stated in an objective, logical way.

The **connotation** of a word is its emotional impact. Some words give rise to positive feelings, while others give rise to negative feelings. Words that evoke mild feelings, or none at all, are said to be neutral.

Consider these synonyms for the neutral word *short*.

> *concise*   *crisp*   *curt*   *terse*

Concise and *crisp* have positive connotations, whereas *curt* and *terse* are negative.

Look at these examples. Notice the different connotations of words with similar denotations.

NEUTRAL	POSITIVE	NEGATIVE
large	capacious	baggy
undo	reverse	negate
plan	devise	scheme

Expressing the Connotation

Read each sentence. Select the word in parentheses that better expresses the connotation (positive, negative, or neutral) given at the beginning of the sentence.

positive **1.** The beach was (**teeming, swarming**) with seagulls and turtles.

positive **2.** Our new puppy has a (**voracious, gluttonous**) appetite and should soon grow into a strong and healthy dog.

negative **3.** Her coaching style is (**forceful, overbearing**) but effective.

negative **4.** Pierre, the so-called writer, claims he has had writer's block for months, but I think he is just (**shiftless, laid-back**).

negative **5.** Several countries agreed to impose a(n) (**prohibition, embargo**) on the sale of arms to the rogue government.

positive **6.** My mother likes to decorate our yard with wind chimes, statues of gnomes, and other (**odd, whimsical**) garden décor.

neutral **7.** Please do not (**taint, alter**) the delicate flavor of the soup with another tablespoon of salt.

neutral **8.** When you consider his many (**quirks, habits**), you must agree that whistling is the least annoying of them all.

Classical Roots

ven, vent—to come

This Latin root appears in **conventional** (page 158). Literally, the word means "referring to or resulting from a coming together." It now has the meaning "customary, common, expected, lacking in originality." Some other words in which this root appears are listed below.

circumvent	eventful	intervene	revenue
convene	eventual	inventive	venue

From the list of words above, choose the one that corresponds to each of the brief definitions below. Write the word in the blank space in the illustrative sentence below the definition. Use a dictionary if necessary.

1. good at making or thinking up new ideas or things; imaginative
The notebooks of Leonardo da Vinci contain abundant evidence of his remarkably inquisitive and _____ intellect.

2. happening at an unspecified time in the future, ultimate
If you stick to an exercise program, you will see _____ improvement in your strength and fitness.

3. to get around or avoid; to defeat, overcome
The pilot was able to _____ the storm by flying farther west.

4. to assemble, come together; to call together
The new book discussion group plans to _____ once a month.

5. full of events or incidents; important
Someone who has led a very _____ life may decide to write an autobiography.

6. to come between; to enter to help settle a dispute
I refuse to _____ in their argument because I do not want to take sides.

7. the place where a crime or cause of legal action occurs; a locality from which a jury is called and in which a trial is held; the scene or locale of any action or event
A defense attorney may sometimes request a change of _____ in order to assure a client a fair trial.

8. income; the income of a government; the yield from property or investment
_____ from the new product line has exceeded the company's expectations.

Read the following passage, taking note of the **boldface** words and their contexts. These words are among those you will be studying in Unit 13. It may help you to complete the exercises in this Unit if you refer to the way the words are used below.

Steven P. Jobs: 1955–2011
<Obituary>

Steven P. Jobs

October 6, 2011

By Tomiko Sato

Steven P. Jobs, the charismatic co-founder of the computer company Apple, Inc., died on Wednesday at the age of 56. The cause of death was complications from pancreatic cancer.

The **enormity** of Mr. Jobs's impact on the many industries he touched still remains to be measured. Over the past 35 years, virtually since the beginning of his adult life, he grew into an iconic figure that symbolized both the computer revolution and everyday life in the digital age. In the entrepreneurial Mr. Jobs, a mastery of technology **dovetailed** almost seamlessly with a passion for stylish, sleek design and an intuitive business sense. To many consumers, the combination proved irresistible, as the loyalty of millions of Apple customers must **attest**.

Steven Paul Jobs was born the son of a young unwed couple in San Francisco, California, on February 24, 1955. Paul and Clara Jobs adopted the boy and raised him in Cupertino, in what is now known as Silicon Valley. The region was shortly to become the world center of computer technology.

The young Steve Jobs grew up with a pronounced rebellious streak, together with a fondness for mischievous pranks—evidence of a **wry** sense of humor. Youth proved no **impediment** to the child's passion for knowledge and electronics, **steadfast** passions that would last a lifetime. In 1969, Steve Jobs befriended Steve Wozniak, who shared his interest in electronic devices. After Jobs dropped out after one semester at Reed College, he and Wozniak joined a computer hobby club together. Soon after, they went into business together. The

Steve Jobs and
Steve Wozniak at the
West Coast Computer
Fair in 1977

Crowds await the opening of the first Apple store in Germany.

two started by assembling personal computers in Mr. Jobs's garage. Thus, in 1976, Apple Computer was born. It was a success from the start.

By 1980, at the age of 25, Mr. Jobs's net worth had exceeded $200 million. Yet numerous twists and turns awaited him in his career. In 1985, after bitter disputes with the Apple Board of Directors, Mr. Jobs was exiled from his own company. Some entrepreneurs in his position might have been expected to become **forlorn** and lose hope. But Mr. Jobs never **faltered** in his determination to be a leader in technology. Without **loitering**, he bought a small computer graphics company and transformed it into the highly successful Pixar Animation Studios. When Pixar went public, Mr. Jobs became a billionaire.

The first Macintosh

In 1997, when Apple's directors again became disenchanted with management, they invited Mr. Jobs back to run the company. By this time, his eccentricities were well known. Never one to suffer fools gladly, Mr. Jobs could be withering in his critiques of colleagues and subordinates: His **pithy** appraisals of their efforts were often characterized as **haughty**, even arrogant,

but Mr. Jobs swiftly grasped the **imperative** at Apple. He created an alliance with a man he once **vilified**, Bill Gates of Microsoft, although both men had accused each other of **plundering** trade secrets and stealing technical know-how. Gates agreed to invest millions in Apple—with Jobs at the helm. In just a few years, Mr. Jobs triumphed with a series of innovative products that became emblematic of an upscale digital lifestyle. Although these products were expensive, consumers must have believed that you get what you pay for: Each device captured the market, aided by Mr. Jobs's legendary ability to **adapt** product launches into epochal events.

Mr. Jobs is survived by his wife, Laurene, his sisters, Mona Simpson and Patty Jobs, and four children.

Audio

For iWords and audio passages, go to SadlierConnect.com.

Definitions

Note the spelling, pronunciation, part(s) of speech, and definition(s) of each of the following words. Then write the appropriate form of the word in the blank space in the illustrative sentence(s) following.

1. attest
(ə test′)

(*v.*) to bear witness, affirm to be true or genuine
I can _____ to the truth of her story because I, too, saw what happened.

2. dovetail
(dəv′ tāl)

(*v.*) to fit together exactly; to connect so as to form a whole; (*n.*) a carpentry figure resembling a dove's tail
We may be able to _____ our activities with theirs if we all plan ahead.
We examined the fine _____ the carpenter used to construct the antique chest.

3. forlorn
(fôr lôrn′)

(*adj.*) totally abandoned and helpless; sad and lonely; wretched or pitiful; almost hopeless
When my best friend moved to another state halfway across the country, I felt extremely _____.

4. imperative
(im per′ ə tiv)

(*adj.*) necessary, urgent; (*n.*) a form of a verb expressing a command; that which is necessary or required
If you step on a rusty nail, it is _____ that you see a doctor as soon as possible.
The writing of a thank-you note to acknowledge a gift or act of kindness is a social _____.

5. loiter
(loi′ tər)

(*v.*) to linger in an aimless way, hang around, dawdle
Some students always _____ in the school yard long after classes are over for the day.

6. malinger
(mə liŋ′ gər)

(*v.*) to pretend illness to avoid duty or work, lie down on the job
If you _____ too often, no one will believe you when you really do fall ill.

7. plunder
(plən′ dər)

(*v.*) to rob by force, especially during wartime; to seize wrongfully; (*n.*) property stolen by force
In the Old West, rustlers _____ ranches and farms for cattle and horses.
Thieves often use a third party called a *fence* to sell jewelry and other _____.

8. steadfast
(sted' fast)

(*adj.*) firmly fixed; constant, not moving or changing
I urge you to be _____ in your efforts
to achieve your goals in life.

9. waif
(wāf)

(*n.*) a person (usually a child) without a home or friend;
a stray person or animal; something that
comes along by chance, a stray bit
The spunky _____ who triumphs over
many hardships is a popular character in film and fiction.

10. wry
(rī)

(*adj.*) twisted, turned to one side; cleverly or grimly humorous
Charles Addams was famous for _____
cartoons chronicling the adventures of a ghoulish family.

Using Context

*For each item, determine whether the **boldface** word from pages 190–191 makes sense in the context of the sentence. Circle the item numbers next to the six sentences in which the words are used correctly.*

1. Except for a small **waif** at the top, the ancient vase was in perfect condition.

2. Our vacation schedules **dovetail** perfectly, so we will be able to plan a trip together.

3. These letters of recommendation strongly **attest** to your qualifications for entering the intensive computer science program.

4. We could not leave the **forlorn** kitten in the parking lot, so we brought it home instead.

5. It's **imperative** that I get my computer fixed because I cannot do any work without it.

6. It was tempting to **malinger** on the beautiful spring day, but I decided to do the right thing and report for work.

7. Who can predict if oil prices will either **plunder** or increase sharply in the next few years?

8. The engineers must **loiter** if they want to show the new product at the sales conference.

9. The **steadfast** light of the candle created an eerie effect, causing the shadows in the room to seem to flicker as well.

10. He is a contemporary poet who brings both **wry** observation and outright humor to his work.

Choosing the Right Word

*Select the **boldface** word that better completes each sentence. You might refer to the passage on pages 188–189 to see how most of these words are used in context. Note that the choices might be related forms of the Unit words.*

1. Most people know the story of Cinderella, a poor, mistreated (**waif, imperative**) who marries a prince and lives happily ever after.

2. Political leaders should feel free to change their minds on specific issues while remaining (**steadfast, wry**) in support of their principles.

3. Monday morning seems to be a favorite time for the employees to practice the fine art of (**plundering, malingering**).

4. The temperaments of the partners in the business (**dovetail, attest**) so well that they can work together without the slightest friction or conflict.

5. Thinking it no crime to borrow from the past, Elizabethan dramatists often (**attested, plundered**) ancient writings for suitable plots.

6. The police sometimes use laws against (**malingering, loitering**) to prevent the gathering of unruly crowds.

7. I believe that it is (**forlorn, imperative**) that we protect our lakes, rivers, and wetlands, as they provide us with clean drinking water.

8. Your outstanding report card and teacher evaluations (**attest, loiter**) to the fact that when you apply yourself, you can be successful.

9. When she learned that she had not been chosen for the job, she made a (**wry, forlorn**) joke, but this did not conceal her deep disappointment.

10. Mutual respect and understanding among all racial and ethnic groups remains a(n) (**imperative, waif**) in the life of this nation.

11. For a time, it was fashionable for supermodels to look like (**waifs, loiterers**), but that undernourished look has lost its appeal.

12. Despite our own exhaustion, we made one final, (**wry, forlorn**) attempt to save the drowning swimmer, but our efforts were to no avail.

Completing the Sentence

Choose the word from the word bank that best completes each of the following sentences. Write the correct word or form of the word in the space provided.

attest	forlorn	loiter	plunder	waif
dovetail	imperative	malinger	steadfast	wry

1. The _____ expressions on the faces of the starving children moved TV audiences to pity and indignation at their plight.

2. Why is it that people tend to _____ in groups in the middle of the sidewalk, blocking the flow of pedestrian traffic?

3. It is _____ for us to produce automobiles that will give us better gas mileage and cause less pollution.

4. In every war, many children are separated from their parents and become homeless _____, begging for food and shelter.

5. They remained my _____ friends, even at a time when it might have been to their advantage to have nothing to do with me.

6. The quick recovery of so many patients _____ to the skill of the hospital staff.

7. The testimony of all the witnesses _____ neatly, forming a strong case against the accused.

8. During our absence, a hungry bear invaded the campsite and _____ our food supply.

9. A fearful young recruit may _____ in an attempt to avoid dangerous duty.

10. The comedian specialized in the kind of _____ humor that gets quiet chuckles from an audience rather than loud bursts of laughter.

Definitions

Note the spelling, pronunciation, part(s) of speech, and definition(s) of each of the following words. Then write the appropriate form of the word in the blank space in the illustrative sentence(s) following.

1. adapt
(ə dapt′)

(*v.*) to adjust or change to suit conditions
As anyone who moves to a new home can tell you, it takes time to _____ to new surroundings.

2. enormity
(i nôr′ mə tē)

(*n.*) the quality of exceeding all moral bounds; an exceedingly evil act; huge size, immensity
The _____ of the disaster shocked and saddened the nation.

3. falter
(fôl′ tər)

(*v.*) to hesitate, stumble, lose courage; to speak hesitatingly; to lose drive, weaken, decline
The newscaster's voice _____ as he announced to the nation that the President was dead.

4. foreboding
(fôr bō′ diŋ)

(*n.*) a warning or feeling that something bad will happen; (*adj.*) marked by fear, ominous
As the hurricane neared, residents of towns along the coast were filled with _____.
All through that long and sleepless night, I was troubled by _____ thoughts.

5. haughty
(hô′ tē)

(*adj.*) chillingly proud and scornful
The _____ tone of voice in which you refused my invitation offended me deeply.

6. impediment
(im ped′ ə mənt)

(*n.*) a physical defect; a hindrance, obstacle
You must not let _____ in your path keep you from pursuing your dreams.

7. pithy
(pith′ ē)

(*adj.*) short but full of meaning
A good editorial should be _____.

8. simper
(sim′ pər)

(*v.*) to smile or speak in a silly, forced way; (*n.*) a silly, forced smile
Strangers may find it easier to _____ about trivial matters than to have a serious conversation.
The camera caught me with a _____ on my face.

9. vaunted
(vônt′ id)

(*adj.*) much boasted about in a vain or swaggering way
The rookie's _____ strength was no match for the veteran's skill and experience.

10. vilify
(vil′ ə fī)

(*v.*) to abuse or belittle unjustly or maliciously
Voters have become thoroughly disgusted with candidates who _____ their rivals' reputations.

Using Context

*For each item, determine whether the **boldface** word from pages 194–195 makes sense in the context of the sentence. Circle the item numbers next to the six sentences in which the words are used correctly.*

1. Most of the extremely successful people in the world have faced failures when trying to accomplish their goals, but they did not allow their determination to **falter** as a result.

2. The teacher insists that his students do all of their writing by hand because he believes working on a computer is an **impediment** to learning.

3. The author hoped to **vilify** her reputation by writing a sequel to her one book that made it onto the bestseller list.

4. As smart as he is, his **haughty** attitude has lost him many job opportunities, because no one wants to work with someone who looks down on others.

5. The **pithy** stare she fixated on me for the rest of class after I had disagreed with her opinion suggested that she now considered me her enemy.

6. As I walked down to the cellar, I nearly ran into the **vaunted** ceiling that was only inches above my head.

7. Many people think he is shallow since he tends to **simper** on about nothing, but in truth he gets nervous around strangers.

8. When I saw the **enormity** of the book, I felt confident I would be able to read it in one sitting.

9. Although the dark clouds in the distance looked **foreboding**, the sun eventually came through and we were able to have a lovely day on the water.

10. When I travel somewhere in a different time zone, I usually don't plan much sightseeing for the first day so that I can **adapt** to the time difference.

Choosing the Right Word

Select the **boldface** word that better completes each sentence. You might refer to the passage on pages 188–189 to see how most of these words are used in context. Note that the choices might be related forms of the Unit words.

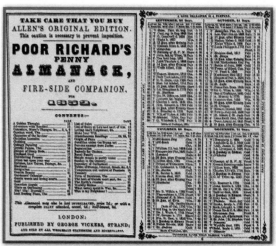

1. The (**pithy, haughty**) advice given by Ben Franklin in *Poor Richard's Almanac* has rarely been equaled for its good common sense.

2. His (**haughty, vaunted**) attitude toward those he considered "beneath him" was a sure sign of lack of breeding and simple good manners.

3. In the opening scene of Shakespeare's *Macbeth*, there is a strong sense of (**foreboding, enormity**) that something terrible is going to happen.

4. The director told him to smile like a "dashing man about town," but all he could do was (**adapt, simper**) like a confused freshman.

5. The (**foreboding, enormity**) of the construction project will provide hundreds of jobs for people over the next five years.

6. "I did what I thought best at the time," the President replied, "and I deeply resent their cowardly attempts to (**vilify, falter**) my actions."

7. Many ad campaigns deliberately (**simper, vaunt**) the superiority of a product over all its competition.

8. No matter how well qualified you may be, an inability to get on well with other people will prove a serious (**foreboding, impediment**) in any field of work.

9. Hordes of savage barbarians swept into the province, committing one (**impediment, enormity**) after another on the defenseless population.

10. People who migrate from the suburbs to the city often find it difficult to (**adapt, vilify**) to the noise and crowded conditions.

11. To (**simper, falter**) now, at the very threshold of victory, would mean that all our earlier struggles and sacrifices had been in vain.

12. Diana was disappointed when she visited the (**vaunted, haughty**) new restaurant, only to find that the food was bland and overpriced.

Completing the Sentence

Choose the word from the word bank that best completes each of the following sentences. Write the correct word or form of the word in the space provided.

adapt	falter	haughty	pithy	vaunted
enormity	foreboding	impediment	simper	vilify

1. Through all the shocks and trials of the Civil War, Abraham Lincoln never _____ in his determination to save the Union.

2. Great skill is required to _____ a novel or short story for the screen.

3. The _____ of the crimes the Nazis committed in the concentration camps horrified the world.

4. After the official had fallen from power, his policies were ridiculed, his motives questioned, and his character _____.

5. Her _____ manner said more clearly than words that she could never associate as an equal with a "peasant" like me.

6. Unless you take steps now to correct your speech _____, it will be a serious hindrance to you throughout your life.

7. When he was caught red-handed in the act of going through my papers, all he did was stand there and _____ foolishly.

8. I appreciate that when I asked for your opinion, you gave it in a few clear, direct, and _____ sentences.

9. When she attempted to order the meal in French, we discovered that her much _____ knowledge of that language made no impression at all on the waiter.

10. When we missed those early foul shots, I had a(n) _____ that the game was going to be a bad one for our team.

Synonyms

*Choose the word or form of the word from this Unit that is the same or most nearly the same in meaning as the **boldface** word or expression in the phrase. Write that word on the line. Use a dictionary if necessary.*

1. told us they had grave **misgivings** _____

2. often **smirks** when embarrassed _____

3. **malign** my good name _____

4. **mesh** the two stories into one _____

5. not permitted to **tarry** after dark _____

6. when complete bed rest is **mandatory** _____

7. did not **stumble** when giving her response _____

8. misinterpreted his **tongue-in-cheek** comments _____

9. gave us a **snobbish** glance _____

10. the **immensity** of the challenge _____

11. **ransacked** the enemy's camp _____

12. the **desolate** factories in a declining town _____

13. took time to **acclimate** to the new school _____

14. **unwavering** devotion to the struggle for equality _____

15. no tolerance for those who **pretend to be ill** _____

Antonyms

*Choose the word or form of the word from this Unit that is most nearly opposite in meaning to the **boldface** word or expression in the phrase. Write that word on the line. Use a dictionary if necessary.*

1. **downplayed** their winning record _____

2. the living conditions of a **socialite** _____

3. a **long-winded** speech _____

4. an **asset** to the team _____

5. **refute** the authenticity of the document _____

Writing: Words in Action

In a brief essay, describe some of the ways—both positive and negative—that high-tech products have had an impact on the way we live today. Support your views with evidence from the reading (pages 188–189) or from your own knowledge or experience. Use three or more words from this Unit.

Vocabulary in Context

*Some of the words you have studied in this Unit appear in **boldface** type. Read the passage below, and then circle the letter of the correct answer for each word as it is used in context.*

Gwen Ifill, an African American journalist who covered the White House, Congress, and national campaigns for three decades, succumbed to uterine cancer at age 61. Born in Jamaica, Queens, Ifill wanted to be a journalist at a young age. Though Ifill's itinerant family occasionally lived in federally subsidized housing, she never saw herself as a pitiable **waif**.

Upon graduating from Simmons College, Ifill worked as a reporter for the *Boston Herald-American* and the *Baltimore Evening Sun.* In 1984, she took a position with the *Washington Post* and covered her first presidential campaign. Her status as a novice meant that during the campaign she often interviewed losing candidates who were filled with **foreboding**.

From 1991 to 1994, Ifill worked for the *New York Times* and covered Bill Clinton's presidency. In 1994, her friend Tim Russert asked her to **adapt** to broadcast journalism and cover Capitol Hill for NBC. Ifill agreed and worked as a political correspondent for NBC. During her tenure, she developed a strong rapport with the audience. In 1999, she accepted a position on PBS's "Washington Week in Review" and "NewsHour."

Ifill never made **vaunted** statements about her career; on the contrary, she was a consummate professional. Colleagues remember Ifill as an unflinching voice who confronted complex issues without a need to **simper**. Even as Ifill's health declined, she didn't **malinger**—rather, she maintained her anchor duties on "Washington Week." Ifill's name will be permanently etched into history as a groundbreaking journalist who overcame considerable barriers.

---

1. What does **waif** most likely mean as it is used in paragraph 1?
   a. a stray person   c. a lonely person
   b. a sad person   d. a creative person

2. What is the meaning of **foreboding** as it is used in paragraph 2?
   a. anticipation   c. premonition
   b. excitement   d. anxiety

3. **Adapt** comes from the Latin word **adaptare. Adaptare** most likely means
   a. to make   c. to decline
   b. to use   d. to fit

4. The word **vaunted** means about the same as
   a. exaggerated   c. meaningless
   b. trumpeted   d. interesting

5. What is the meaning of **simper** as it is used in paragraph 4?
   a. speak in a silly way   c. speak in an angry way
   b. speak in a mocking way   d. speak in a foolish way

6. Which does **malinger** most likely mean as it is used in paragraph 4?
   a. finish a job   c. lie down on the job
   b. do a careless job   d. take another job

Read the following passage, taking note of the **boldface** words and their contexts. These words are among those you will be studying in Unit 14. It may help you to complete the exercises in this Unit if you refer to the way the words are used below.

Now Arriving on Track 1: New York Dry Goods
<Letter>

The last spike of the Transcontinental Railroad is driven at Promontory, Utah, on May 10, 1869.

In the United States in 1862, plans began to develop for building a railroad linking the east coast and the west coast. The Transcontinental Railroad, finished in 1869, would span the country and forever change travel and life in the United States.

September 12, 1869

Dear William:

I was pleased to receive your letter inquiring about our operations here in San Francisco. Business has flourished since I opened our western office over a decade ago. The frenzy of the gold rush days has subsided, but there is now sufficient population and enterprise in our region to support a growing commerce. There is steady demand for the dry goods I import from your father's New York warehouse. From time to time, our business is **amplified** by new railroad construction, a new discovery of silver, or a new mine.

I agree with your assessment of our prospects. The completion of the Pacific Railroad, at last linking the coasts of our great nation, marks a new **epoch** in commerce. Yet it would be **naive** to depend entirely on rail transport for our imports anytime soon, or to expect the oceanic traffic to be **obliterated**. Already, the steamers have lowered their prices. Of course, where time is of the essence, we will prefer the overland route. I am **gratified** to report that our first shipments arrived at the new Alameda station. This transcontinental railroad is a sign of progress to come and of a seemingly **infinite** potential in this country. It will drive the growth of commerce. But it is also a measure of what has already been achieved.

Would the great men who invested their wealth in this project have **estranged** themselves from their capital if there were not already a great demand for transport across the continent?

As to your prospects, there is always a place for you here, should you decide to come to California and add your strength to the pursuit of our **kindred** interests. The work in our office is for the most part quite **tedious**, though you're welcome to a share if your tastes run to the **bland**. You may prefer to manage shipments to the **vendors** and merchants we supply in California, Utah, and Nevada. I confess I've grown tired of dealings with customers. Too many of them prove **arrogant** and **irascible**. I just overheard a local man arguing with our shopkeeper over the price of some fine linen. The way he put on airs, even pretending the cloth was defective, calls to mind the old saying, the bigger the hat, the smaller the farm. I'd be relieved to put the storefront's oversight in your hands. If you have some other role in mind, we can find a **niche** that suits you.

Recently, I spoke with William Ralston. He had a hand in establishing the Bank of California some five years ago. He is keen to see San Francisco blossom into a great city and says that recent growth in local manufacturing will continue. The city itself, hardly more than a clutter of canvass tents and **ramshackle** houses when I arrived, has matured into a fine urban center. There are many elegant homes, and entertainments enough to keep a young man like yourself occupied in your leisure hours. This year saw the opening of the California Theater, another of Mr. Ralston's projects, which makes an impressive addition to our city life.

I await word of your decision.

Affectionately,
Uncle Albert

Audio

For iWords and audio passages, go to SadlierConnect.com.

Steamer Day, San Francisco, California, 1866

Definitions

Note the spelling, pronunciation, part(s) of speech, and definition(s) of each of the following words. Then write the appropriate form of the word in the blank space in the illustrative sentence(s) following.

1. armistice
(är′ mə stis)

(*n.*) a temporary peace, halt in fighting
Diplomats hope to negotiate an _____ between the warring nations.

2. bland
(bland)

(*adj.*) gentle, soothing, mild; lacking interest or taste
Some people prefer to live in a place where the climate is _____ and unchanging all year-round.

3. disclaim
(dis klām′)

(*v.*) to deny interest in or connection with; to give up all claim to
Both candidates _____ any ties to special-interest groups.

4. gratify
(grat′ ə fī)

(*v.*) to please, satisfy; to indulge or humor
Experts advise parents not to _____ a child's every whim.

5. infinite
(in′ fə nit)

(*adj.*) exceedingly great, inexhaustible, without limit, endless; (*n.*, preceded by *the*) an incalculable number, the concept of infinity; (cap. *I*) a name for God
It may take _____ patience to be a parent, but the rewards are equally great.
A belief in the _____ is a source of comfort and hope to many people who are in distress.

6. naive
(na ēv′)

(*adj.*) innocent, unsophisticated, showing lack of worldly knowledge and experience
A _____ person may be easily taken in by get-rich-quick schemes.

7. niche
(nich)

(*n.*) a decorative recess in a wall; a suitable place or position for a person or thing
That _____ in the hallway is a perfect spot for a vase of fresh flowers.

8. ransack
(ran′ sak)

(*v.*) to search or examine thoroughly; to rob, plunder
Robbers _____ the house for cash and other valuables.

9. **solvent**
(säl′ vənt)

(*adj.*) able to meet one's financial obligations; having the power to dissolve other substances; (*n.*) a liquid used to dissolve other substances; something that solves, explains, eliminates, or softens

If you want to remain _____, set a budget and stick to it.

To remove tar and paint from your hands, you may have to use a _____.

10. **tedious**
(tē′ dē əs)

(*adj.*) long and tiresome

Sometimes I find it hard to pay close attention to a _____ lecture.

Using Context

*For each item, determine whether the **boldface** word from pages 202–203 makes sense in the context of the sentence. Circle the item numbers next to the six sentences in which the words are used correctly.*

1. What is the correct way to dispose of a powerful household **solvent**, such as turpentine or nail polish remover?

2. The nimble dancer so effortlessly performed the leaps that it looked nearly **tedious**.

3. To make that bowl of oatmeal taste less **bland**, you can add some fruit or cinnamon sugar.

4. Rather than **ransack** the room to find the missing wallet, let's search methodically.

5. If we put off making repairs in the plumbing system now, the problems will **gratify** and become more costly to fix later on.

6. World War I officially ended when an **armistice** was signed on November 11, 1918.

7. It is a good idea to practice before you **disclaim** your speech in front of an audience.

8. Have you ever heard the theory stating that if a monkey could hit keys on a keyboard for an **infinite** amount of time, it would eventually type the complete works of William Shakespeare?

9. In George Orwell's *Animal Farm*, a group of **naive** farmyard characters are exploited by a group of greedy, power-hungry ones.

10. The **niche** of dark clouds in the sky was a sure sign that a thunderstorm was coming.

Choosing the Right Word

*Select the **boldface** word that better completes each sentence. You might refer to the passage on pages 200–201 to see how most of these words are used in context. Note that the choices might be related forms of the Unit words.*

1. In Dickens's novel *Oliver Twist*, the protagonist is so (**naive, tedious**) that he does not understand that he is being trained to become a pickpocket.

2. They claim to have "buried the hatchet," but I fear they have only declared a temporary (**solvent, armistice**) in their feud.

3. Although I was furious, I faced my accusers with a (**tedious, bland**) smile.

4. I (**ransacked, gratified**) my brain feverishly, but I was unable to find any way out of the difficulty.

5. You will learn that nothing is more (**disclaiming, gratifying**) than to face a problem squarely, analyze it clearly, and resolve it successfully.

6. He found a comfortable (**niche, armistice**) for himself at a bank and worked there quite happily for more than 40 years.

7. The business had been losing money for years; but thanks to new management, it is once again (**infinite, solvent**).

8. Rather than (**disclaim, ransack**) their religious faiths, many Protestants, Catholics, and Jews left Europe to settle in the New World.

9. My next-door neighbor is a(n) (**tedious, infinite**) individual with a remarkable talent for boring me out of my wits.

10. Can anyone be so (**naive, bland**) as to believe that all famous people who endorse products on TV actually use those products?

11. Rioters smashed windows and (**disclaimed, ransacked**) government offices as they attempted to overthrow the dictator.

12. We are now learning the hard way that our energy sources are not (**infinite, bland**) and that we will have to use them carefully.

Completing the Sentence

Choose the word from the word bank that best completes each of the following sentences. Write the correct word or form of the word in the space provided.

armistice	disclaim	infinite	niche	solvent
bland	gratify	naive	ransack	tedious

1. Now that a(n) _____ has finally been arranged, the even more difficult job of making a lasting peace must begin.

2. Optimists believe that the world is ultimately marked by _____ power and goodness.

3. "A dinner that is truly well prepared _____ the eye as well as the palate," a famous chef once remarked.

4. Along the walls of the palace, there were _____ in which statues had been placed.

5. How could you have been so _____ and foolish as to take their compliments seriously?

6. After four hours of doing the same small task over and over again, I began to find my new job _____.

7. I've been broke for so long that I'm afraid I won't know how to behave when I find myself _____ again.

8. Because I was obeying all traffic regulations at the time the accident occurred, I _____ responsibility for it.

9. After eating so much highly spiced food while on vacation, I craved some pleasantly _____ home cooking.

10. When the electric power failed, we _____ the kitchen to find candles and matches.

Definitions

Note the spelling, pronunciation, part(s) of speech, and definition(s) of each of the following words. Then write the appropriate form of the word in the blank space in the illustrative sentence(s) following.

1. amplify
(am′ plə fī)

(*v.*) to make stronger, larger, greater, louder, or the like
Some court rulings _____ the authority of the individual states.

2. arrogant
(ar′ ə gənt)

(*adj.*) haughty, too convinced of one's own importance
An _____ individual is likely to find it difficult to work as part of a team.

3. epoch
(ep′ ək)

(*n.*) a distinct period of time, age
The mapping of the human genetic code marked the start of a promising new _____ in medicine.

4. estrange
(e strănj′)

(*v.*) to drift apart or become unfriendly; to cause such a separation; to remove or keep at a distance
A long and bitter feud may _____ a family that was once close-knit.

5. irascible
(ir as′ ə bəl)

(*adj.*) easily made angry, hot-tempered
Working for an _____ boss can be very difficult indeed.

6. kindred
(kin′ drəd)

(*n.*) a person's relatives; a family relationship;
(*adj.*) related by blood; like, similar
If you have any long-lost _____, you may be able to use the Internet to locate them.
People who feel that they are _____ spirits usually have many interests in common.

7. obliterate
(ə blit′ ə rāt)

(*v.*) to blot out completely, destroy utterly
An earthquake can _____ large portions of a major city in a matter of minutes.

8. ramshackle
(ram′ shak əl)

(*adj.*) appearing ready to collapse, loose and shaky
A few _____ buildings are all that remain of the old mining town.

9. rote
(rōt)

(*n.*) unthinking routine or repetition, a fixed or mechanical way of doing something; (*adj.*) based on a mechanical routine

Most people learn to type by _____.

_____ memorization can be helpful when you begin to study a foreign language.

10. vendor
(ven′ dər)

(*n.*) a person who sells something

If the appliance you purchased turns out to be defective, you should return it to the _____.

Using Context

*For each item, determine whether the **boldface** word from pages 206–207 makes sense in the context of the sentence. Circle the item numbers next to the six sentences in which the words are used correctly.*

1. This **ramshackle** structure before you was once the most opulent hotel in town.

2. The tour guide had to use a loudspeaker to **amplify** his voice on the crowded bus.

3. The **epoch** between when I submitted my college application and when I heard that I had been accepted seemed like a lifetime, but in truth it was only about a month.

4. Since the reviews of the book were so great, I was surprised that I found the novel so **irascible** that I could barely remember the plot right after I finished it.

5. Though she was once humble and open-minded, the promotion she received has made her **arrogant** and infuriating to work with.

6. The two friends recognized each other as **kindred** spirits when they talked for hours about their common interests the first night they met.

7. Despite my insistence that I would not buy anything at the fair, I found myself running up to each **vendor** to see what trinkets they had for sale.

8. I find that spending time in nature can always **obliterate** my energy and awaken my senses.

9. The new reality show will try to **estrange** adopted children with their birth parents and broadcast the reunions live.

10. When I had a teacher who encouraged me to focus on understanding the scientific concepts rather than memorizing terms by **rote**, I started to do much better in the class.

Choosing the Right Word

*Select the **boldface** word that better completes each sentence. You might refer to the passage on pages 200–201 to see how most of these words are used in context. Note that the choices might be related forms of the Unit words.*

1. Every week she meets with a small circle of (**ramshackle, kindred**) souls whose greatest interest in life is the music of Johann Sebastian Bach.

2. The beginning of commercial television in the 1940s marked a revolutionary (**vendor, epoch**) in the history of mass communications.

3. The excuse that he offered for his absence was so (**arrogant, ramshackle**) and improbable that it fell apart as soon as we looked into it.

4. I am willing to forgive you, but I don't know if I can ever (**obliterate, estrange**) the memory of your dishonesty from my mind.

5. The spirit of the new law to protect consumers is not "Let the buyer beware" but, rather, "Let the (**vendor, epoch**) beware."

6. Over the years, the vigorous foreign policy that this country pursued greatly (**amplified, estranged**) our role in world affairs.

7. Whenever my supervisor gets into one of his (**ramshackle, irascible**) moods, I know that I'm in for some high drama before the day is out.

8. What is important for the children is not a(n) (**irascible, rote**) recital of the poem but an understanding of what the words really mean.

9. The job of a mediator is to help (**kindred, estranged**) parties find a basis for settling their differences.

10. A person who behaves with (**kindred, arrogant**) disregard for the feelings of others is likely to have very few friends.

11. Some people are worried that sizable asteroids could hit Earth and (**obliterate, ramshackle**) entire cities.

12. Several (**vendors, epochs**) at the fair were giving away free samples to entice customers to buy their wares.

Completing the Sentence

Choose the word from the word bank that best completes each of the following sentences. Write the correct word or form of the word in the space provided.

amplify	epoch	irascible	obliterate	rote
arrogant	estrange	kindred	ramshackle	vendor

1. He used to be a modest, likable fellow, but now that he has inherited some money, his manner has become exceedingly _____ and offensive.

2. Although she had been separated from her family for years, at her hour of need her _____ came to her aid.

3. I think the vivid phrase "having a short fuse" aptly describes my neighbor's _____ temperament.

4. We did not realize how poor the people in that isolated region were until we saw the _____ huts in which they were living.

5. "You should understand the reason for each step in the problem," our math teacher said, "not simply do the steps by _____."

6. "Unless we learn to control nuclear weapons," the speaker said, "they may _____ the human race."

7. The tinkling bell of the ice-cream _____ making his way through the streets is a pleasant sound on a summer evening.

8. Increasing dissatisfaction with the direction her political party was taking slowly _____ her from it.

9. The Declaration of Independence's assertion that "all men are created equal" marked a new _____ in world history.

10. We want to download an application that will _____ our sound effects without distorting them.

Synonyms

*Choose the word or form of the word from this Unit that is the same or most nearly the same in meaning as the **boldface** word or expression in the phrase. Write that word on the line. Use a dictionary if necessary.*

1. **routine** performance of the task _____
2. **disavow** all stories related to the scandal _____
3. unwilling to **alienate** supporters _____
4. **expunged** the evidence _____
5. **rummaged** the trash for clues _____
6. feared entering the **dilapidated** house _____
7. **magnify** the image _____
8. a party for her distant **relations** _____
9. able to fool the **unsophisticated** youngster _____
10. the **cantankerous** old man _____
11. found her **calling** at a young age _____
12. the royals' **high-handed** treatment of others _____
13. during an **era** of peace and prosperity _____
14. found the opera **dull** _____
15. a **merchant** with an old-fashioned pushcart _____

Antonyms

*Choose the word or form of the word from this Unit that is most nearly opposite in meaning to the **boldface** word or expression in the phrase. Write that word on the line. Use a dictionary if necessary.*

1. a report that the applicant is **completely broke** _____
2. a **conflict** in the Middle East _____
3. a **disappointing** meal _____
4. corrected the seasoning of the **spicy** dish _____
5. a **limited** number of choices _____

Writing: Words in Action

Suppose you are William's friend, and you have decided to head west. You want to persuade William to join you on the trip. Write a letter using examples from your reading (pages 200–201), personal experiences, and prior knowledge to convince him. Use three or more words from this Unit.

Vocabulary in Context

*Some of the words you have studied in this Unit appear in **boldface** type. Read the passage below, and then circle the letter of the correct answer for each word as it is used in context.*

After the **armistice** ending the Mexican-American War in 1848, Mexico ceded the territory that is now California to the United States. Early the same year, gold was discovered at Sutter's Mill on the American River near Sacramento. Despite efforts to **disclaim** this discovery, word spread like wildfire. Within a year, 300,000 people poured into California from the United States and from many foreign lands, some as distant as Australia and China. Most of these newcomers were determined to **ransack** every square inch of the territory in the hope of striking it rich.

Sadly, many "forty-niners," as they came to be known, could not remain **solvent** and went bust. Mining camps became legendary for lawlessness and disorder. Failures and violence, however, did little to diminish the soaring dreams of the **epoch**.

By 1850, California had grown so fast that demands for statehood multiplied. High on the agenda of statehood supporters was the need for law enforcement and governmental institutions such as courts and schools.

Rote memorization of American history can offer a general idea of the daunting issues involved with statehood. California was poised to enter the Union as a free state, with a constitution forbidding slavery. Ever since the Missouri Compromise of 1820, when Missouri and Maine had entered the Union as a slave state and free state, respectively, American politicians had focused on maintaining an equal balance between the states allowing slavery and the states that banned it. With California statehood, through the efforts of Senator Henry Clay of Kentucky, the Compromise of 1850 preserved the peace, but only for a little more than a decade.

---

1. What is the meaning of **armistice** as it is used in paragraph 1?
 a. negotiation   c. cease-fire
 b. treaty   d. collapse

2. What is the meaning of **disclaim** as it is used in paragraph 1?
 a. negate   c. explain
 b. publicize   d. clarify

3. The word **ransack** means about the same as
 a. auction   c. scour
 b. analyze   d. exclude

4. Which word means the same as **solvent** as it is used in paragraph 2?
 a. respected   c. bankrupt
 b. wealthy   d. sound

5. **Epoch** comes from the Greek word **epokhe. Epokhe** most likely means
 a. point in time   c. elite
 b. society   d. middle class

6. What does **rote** most likely mean as it is used in paragraph 4?
 a. accurate   c. mechanical
 b. intermittent   d. tedious

Read the following passage, taking note of the **boldface** words and their contexts. These words are among those you will be studying in Unit 15. It may help you to complete the exercises in this Unit if you refer to the way the words are used below.

Muckraking Journalist Ida M. Tarbell
<Biographical Sketch>

Ida M. Tarbell, c. 1904

Ida M. Tarbell was a pioneering investigative journalist. Her 1902–1904 magazine serial exposé, "The History of the Standard Oil Company," did much to reform the United States oil industry. It changed the face of journalism and was the **crucial** catalyst for the breakup of the Standard Oil Trust in 1911. Her nineteen-part **opus** painted a scathing portrait of the shady practices of Standard Oil and its founder and president, John D. Rockefeller, America's first billionaire.

That it was a woman who helped bring down an oil empire may have surprised some in an era when women were still regarded as the "weaker sex." But it did not surprise those who knew Ida Tarbell. While outwardly modest, with the **veneer** of a polite and proper lady, Tarbell **embodied** daring and courage. She had a passion for exposing the truth.

She also claimed an oil-related **heritage**. Tarbell was born in 1857 in Hatch Hollow, Pennsylvania. Her father became an independent oil producer and refiner in the state's oil-rich region. Young Ida watched as he lost his business due to Rockefeller's **mercenary** practices, which involved **reciprocal** agreements between powerful railroad interests and a select group of large oil refiners. These tactics effectively shut out smaller companies.

Tarbell never forgot the **fiasco** that had **befallen** her father. It played a key role in shaping her later career. After high school, she attended Allegheny College (she was the sole female in her freshman class in 1876). She taught science briefly before becoming a writer. She moved to Paris, France, to work on a biography of a French revolutionary, and returned home at the invitation of a publisher who was starting a political and literary magazine.

Tarbell composed acclaimed pieces for the monthly *McClure's Magazine* on Napoleon Bonaparte and Abraham Lincoln. But this was just a dry run. It was her carefully researched and **rational** articles on illicit industrial practices—**garnished** with her trademark spirited insights—that made her famous. And it proclaimed the era of the Progressive and the muckraker (a term made popular by President Theodore Roosevelt to describe how the journalists "dug up the dirt" on those they investigated).

McClure's Magazine was a leading publisher of muckraking articles.
John D. Rockefeller was a prime target of Ida M. Tarbell's groundbreaking journalism.

Shrugging off the **strictures** of conventional journalism, Tarbell and her muckraking cohorts dug deep to uncover injustice and corruption. They avoided the moral **abyss** of yellow journalism, which focused on sensationalism rather than truth. Instead, they presented facts to win over converts to the Progressive cause, which fought for political reform, better working conditions, and civil rights. They targeted hazardous conditions in coal mines, issues of child labor, disease-ridden hospitals, filthy and overcrowded slums, fake patent medicines, and more. Their articles **exasperated** politicians, business tycoons, and bigwigs whose illegal or **negligent** practices were investigated. But they thrilled the public. They also galvanized official investigations and prompted legal reforms. Tarbell's celebrated series of articles on Standard Oil were the opening salvo. A 1911 Supreme Court decision dissolved the oil monopoly into numerous smaller companies. Many of these companies are still active today. The work of the muckrakers led to stricter child labor laws and the passage of the Pure Food and Drug Act of 1906. The muckrakers influenced how investigative reporters work to this day.

Ida Tarbell lived to the age of 84, writing almost up to the day she died. She gained an international reputation as a writer, historian, and editor.

Audio

For iWords and audio passages, go to SadlierConnect.com.

Definitions

Note the spelling, pronunciation, part(s) of speech, and definition(s) of each of the following words. Then write the appropriate form of the word in the blank space in the illustrative sentence(s) following.

1. abyss
(ə bis′)

(*n.*) a deep or bottomless pit
Mountain climbers must take great care lest they slip and fall into an _____.

2. crucial
(krü′ shəl)

(*adj.*) of supreme importance, decisive, critical
In many adventure films, the hero always arrives just at the _____ moment.

3. embody
(em bäd′ ē)

(*v.*) to give form to; to incorporate, include; to personify
The villain in a melodrama _____ cold-blooded ruthlessness.

4. fiasco
(fē as′ kō)

(*n.*) the complete collapse or failure of a project
With the bases loaded, our star pitcher gave up a home run, turning a close game into a _____.

5. garnish
(gär′ nish)

(*v.*) to adorn or decorate, especially food; (*n.*) an ornament or decoration, especially for food
The chef _____ our salad with colorful edible flowers.
When it comes to mystery novels, I prefer those that have a _____ of wit.

6. negligent
(neg′ lə jənt)

(*adj.*) marked by carelessness or indifference; failing to do what should be done
A driver who is _____ about obeying traffic regulations may end up causing an accident.

7. oblivion
(ə bliv′ ē ən)

(*n.*) forgetfulness, disregard; a state of being forgotten; an amnesty, general pardon
Down through the ages, poets have described sleep as a kind of _____ that brings relief from woe.

8. pallid
(pal′ id)

(*adj.*) pale, lacking color; weak and lifeless
A long illness may leave a person looking extremely frail and _____.

9. **parable**
(par′ ə bəl)

(*n.*) a short narrative designed to teach a moral lesson
Sermons are often based on _____
from the New Testament.

10. **reciprocal**
(ri sip′ rə kəl)

(*adj.*) shared; involving give-and-take between two
persons or things; working in both directions; (*n.*) (*math*) a
number that, when multiplied by another number, gives 1
A _____ understanding of each other's
likes and dislikes is important in a close friendship.
The fraction $\frac{4}{3}$ is the _____
of the fraction $\frac{3}{4}$.

Using Context

*For each item, determine whether the **boldface** word from pages 214–215 makes sense in the context of the sentence. Circle the item numbers next to the six sentences in which the words are used correctly.*

1. Some of the gods and goddesses in Greek mythology **embody** a particular strength or quality, such as wisdom, beauty, or courage in warfare.

2. When the concert ended, members of the audience kept cheering, signaling that they expected the band to perform one more song as a **fiasco**.

3. You can make a fresh and tasty tomato sauce with just three **crucial** ingredients: olive oil, garlic, and ripe tomatoes.

4. The radish that was arranged to look like a flower was a delightful **garnish**.

5. Does a **parable** always teach a lesson that is religious in nature?

6. A coral island forms when an **abyss** rises out of the sea.

7. You can tell by the drooping leaves and dry soil that we have been **negligent** about watering the houseplants.

8. The **oblivion** that surrounds our planet is made up chiefly of nitrogen and oxygen.

9. Signs on the road are most often yellow or orange, since these **pallid** colors are easily seen.

10. In a **reciprocal** arrangement, the dairy farmers provided milk to the cheese makers, and the cheese makers shared their finished product with the farmers.

Choosing the Right Word

*Select the **boldface** word that better completes each sentence. You might refer to the passage on pages 212–213 to see how most of these words are used in context. Note that the choices might be related forms of the Unit words.*

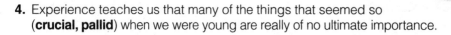

1. My uncle, who was a West Point graduate, (**embodied, garnished**) all the qualities suggested by the phrase "an officer and a gentleman."

2. If you are (**reciprocal, negligent**) about small sums of money, you may find that you will never have any large sums to worry about.

3. After his crushing defeat in the election, the candidate returned to his hometown and disappeared into (**fiasco, oblivion**).

4. Experience teaches us that many of the things that seemed so (**crucial, pallid**) when we were young are really of no ultimate importance.

5. The plan of the two schools to exchange members of their faculties proved to be of (**pallid, reciprocal**) advantage.

6. Marion turned (**negligent, pallid**) when she received the news that her grandfather had suffered a stroke.

7. I spent months planning the fund-raiser, but it turned out to be a (**garnish, fiasco**): the guest speaker cancelled at the last minute, and the band was two hours late.

8. "The heroism of these brave men and women speaks for itself and needs no (**oblivion, garnishing**)," said the senator.

9. What a relief to turn from those (**pallid, negligent**) little tales to the lively, vigorous, earthy stories of Mark Twain.

10. Such familiar stories as "Little Red Riding Hood" are really (**parables, fiascos**) that tell a child something about the conditions of human life.

11. Isn't it tragic that the religious groups fighting each other are separated by a(n) (**parable, abyss**) of misunderstanding?

12. When the court found that the car company had been (**negligent, crucial**)— selling cars with substandard brakes—it was ordered to pay millions in fines.

Completing the Sentence

Choose the word from the word bank that best completes each of the following sentences. Write the correct word or form of the word in the space provided.

abyss	embody	garnish	oblivion	parable
crucial	fiasco	negligent	pallid	reciprocal

1. Winston Churchill warned the English people that if they gave in to the Nazis, they would "sink into the _____ of a new Dark Age."

2. My mother doesn't think that a plate of food is ready to serve unless she has _____ it with a sprig of parsley or a slice of tomato.

3. She was a famous writer in her own day, but her novels and stories have now passed into _____.

4. In high school, you will make many decisions _____ to your future, but determining what to wear to the prom is not one of them.

5. The judge imposed a heavy fine on the _____ landlord who had failed to provide heat during the cold weather.

6. The ancient story of the Prodigal Son is a(n) _____ that helps people understand problems and situations of present-day life.

7. The brief code of laws known as the Ten Commandments _____ basic moral values.

8. The old adage "I'll scratch your back if you'll scratch mine" aptly describes the kind of _____ arrangement he has in mind.

9. In no time at all, poor management turned what should have been a surefire success into a costly _____.

10. Of course she didn't look well after her stay in the hospital, but a few days at the beach took care of that _____ complexion.

Definitions

Note the spelling, pronunciation, part(s) of speech, and definition(s) of each of the following words. Then write the appropriate form of the word in the blank space in the illustrative sentence(s) following.

---

1. befall
(bi fôl')

(*v.*) to happen, occur; to happen to

It is only natural to worry from time to time about the ills that may someday _____ us.

---

2. dregs
(dregz)

(*n. pl.*) the last remaining part; the part of least worth

The _____ of bitterness are all that remain of our former friendship.

---

3. exasperate
(eg zas' pə rāt)

(*v.*) to irritate, annoy, or anger

Small children sometimes _____ adults with endless questions.

---

4. heritage
(her' ə tij)

(*n.*) an inheritance; a birthright

A rich _____ of human history and creativity is housed in the world's libraries and museums.

---

5. inert
(in ərt')

(*adj.*) lifeless, unable to move or act; slow, inactive

In order to keep patients _____ during surgery, doctors use various general anesthetics.

---

6. mercenary
(mər' sə ner ē)

(*adj.*) acting or working for self-gain only; (*n.*) a hired soldier, a soldier of fortune

A fortune hunter's motives are _____ rather than romantic.

A country that does not have a standing army may need to call upon _____ to fight in its wars.

---

7. opus
(ō' pəs)

(*n.*) an impressive piece of work, especially a musical composition or other work of art

Many scholars consider Michelangelo's Sistine Chapel paintings to be his greatest _____.

---

8. rational
(rash' ə nəl)

(*adj.*) based on reasoning; able to make use of reason; sensible or reasonable

Calm and _____ analysis should lead you to a solution to most problems.

---

9. stricture
(strik′ chər)

(*n.*) a limitation or restriction; a criticism;
(*medicine*) a narrowing of a passage in the body
Most religions impose dietary _____
of some sort on their followers.

10. veneer
(və nēr′)

(*n.*) a thin outer layer; a surface appearance
or decoration; (*v.*) to cover with a thin layer
Some people may adopt a thin _____
of friendliness to hide their true feelings toward others.
Furniture makers often _____ sturdy
but common wood with a finer, more costly variety.

Using Context

*For each item, determine whether the **boldface** word from pages 218–219 makes sense in the context of the sentence. Circle the item numbers next to the six sentences in which the words are used correctly.*

1. The child finally began to **exasperate** after crying for hours and drifted off to sleep.

2. The audience reacted to the finale with such **opus** that the standing ovation did not end for nearly half an hour.

3. I became **inert** with fear when I heard something else moving about in the house, until I realized it was just the cat and the tension left my body.

4. We were impressed by the **veneer** with which the principal spoke to us, not trying to hide any facts of the recent debacle and speaking to us like adults.

5. Our **mercenary** old neighbor will speak to other people only to complain.

6. As impressive as your **heritage** may be, you should try to live up to your good name rather than just boasting about it.

7. As much as I appreciate his **rational** point of view, I wish he would sometimes play along with my idealistic dreams.

8. The parents placed a **stricture** on how many sweets their children could eat.

9. Even though bad events can happen to anyone, it is of no use to sit around worrying about what may or may not **befall** us.

10. Those who see homeless people as the **dregs** of society usually don't take time to consider what misfortunes may have led them to that situation.

Choosing the Right Word

*Select the **boldface** word that better completes each sentence. You might refer to the passage on pages 212–213 to see how most of these words are used in context. Note that the choices might be related forms of the Unit words.*

1. In this early novel by Dickens, we have a(n) (**stricture, opus**) that gives us a wonderful picture of life in nineteenth-century England.

2. Her constant chattering while I'm trying to do my vocabulary exercises (**exasperates, befalls**) me more than I can say.

3. Once the war had been won, the victors laid aside their high-minded ideals and became involved in a (**mercenary, rational**) squabble over the spoils.

4. Using the (**dregs, veneer**) in the teacup, the fortune teller gave the young woman a reading about her happiness.

5. Any significant (**dregs, stricture**) of the passages leading to the heart will hinder the normal flow of blood to that organ and cause cardiac arrest.

6. There are times when it is good to let your imagination run free, instead of trying to be strictly (**rational, inert**).

7. Because decent people would have nothing to do with him, he soon began to associate with the (**dregs, heritages**) of humanity.

8. If our leadership is timid and (**mercenary, inert**), we will never be able to solve the great problems that face us.

9. It's hard for people to admit that some of the misfortunes that (**befall, exasperate**) them are really their own fault.

10. Underneath the (**veneer, stricture**) of her polished manners, we recognized the down-to-earth young woman we had known in earlier years.

11. A descendant of one of the Founding Fathers of this country, she strove all her life to live up to her distinguished (**opus, heritage**).

12. During the Revolutionary War, some 30,000 (**dregs, mercenaries**) fought with the British troops.

Completing the Sentence

Choose the word from the word bank that best completes each of the following sentences. Write the correct word or form of the word in the space provided.

| befall | exasperate | inert | opus | stricture |
| dregs | heritage | mercenary | rational | veneer |

1. During her confinement in a prisoner-of-war camp, she drained the cup of human suffering to the _____.

2. Astrologers claim that they can discover what will _____ a person by studying the movements of various heavenly bodies.

3. The administration intends to propose legislation to cut back on customs duties and relax other _____ on foreign trade.

4. In this third century of our nation's history, let us continue to safeguard our _____ of freedom.

5. Without pretending that he cared about the public welfare, he told us frankly that his interest in the project was purely _____.

6. Nothing _____ me more than neighbors who play loud music outdoors late at night.

7. Would you like your new desk finished with a(n) _____ of walnut, maple, or mahogany?

8. A number of famous Roman emperors were clearly madmen for whose actions no _____ explanation can possibly be devised.

9. Many composers don't publish their works in the order in which they are written, so the number given to a particular _____ might not tell much about the date of its composition.

10. To our dismay, the running back didn't get to his feet after being tackled but instead lay _____ on the field.

Synonyms

*Choose the word or form of the word from this Unit that is the same or most nearly the same in meaning as the **boldface** word or expression in the phrase. Write that word on the line. Use a dictionary if necessary.*

1. a **teaching tale** with an important message   _____

2. one who **exemplifies** courage and strength   _____

3. **embellish** with parsley   _____

4. will remain **still** until pushed   _____

5. a total **disaster**   _____

6. found by the court to be **derelict**   _____

7. had a distinguished **pedigree**   _____

8. a **shared** gesture of kindness   _____

9. a desk finished in an oak **overlay**   _____

10. a thoroughly selfish and **greedy** individual   _____

11. wondering what will **happen to** our town   _____

12. a bad habit that truly **vexes** me   _____

13. inhibited by the **restraints** of our coach's rules   _____

14. in a state of **unconsciousness**   _____

15. the artist's most brilliant **work**   _____

Antonyms

*Choose the word or form of the word from this Unit that is most nearly opposite in meaning to the **boldface** word or expression in the phrase. Write that word on the line. Use a dictionary if necessary.*

1. an **inconsequential** role in the play   _____

2. a place frequented by the **upper crust** of society   _____

3. known to be **illogical**   _____

4. approached what felt like the **summit**   _____

5. **rosy** cheeks due to illness   _____

Writing: Words in Action

Think about how the determination of just one person was able to dissolve the powerful Standard Oil Trust. Write a brief report describing how investigative journalists such as Ida Tarbell can help bring about social reform. Use examples from your reading (pages 212–213), observations, and three or more words from this Unit.

Vocabulary in Context

*Some of the words you have studied in this Unit appear in **boldface** type. Read the passage below, and then circle the letter of the correct answer for each word as it is used in context.*

"Ever since our earliest ancestors first gazed up into the night sky billions of years ago, humankind has been wondering if any of those motionless myriads of stars and planets could possibly be inhabited by beings like ourselves. As they stared up, they must have wondered if beings of a faraway world were staring back down at them. Their speculations might easily have been lost in the **oblivion** of time, but now it appears that those first humans were right to wonder. After twelve years of secret research, a team of Australian astrophysicists led by Professor Aldon Pomfrey of the University of Woomera, South Australia, has made a discovery so shocking that their government has forbidden them to publish their findings."

Everyone who uses the Internet is familiar with this kind of nonsensical **opus**. It might have a thin veneer of plausibility, but it defies rational consideration. Nobody knows what our "earliest ancestors" thought as they looked into the sky and **pallid** speculation is not enough to base a news story on. Early humans certainly would have noticed, however, that those points of light were not **inert**. A couple of minutes' research shows there is no Professor Aldon Pomfrey, and no university in Woomera. The **parable** is, don't believe everything you read.

Nevertheless, there are people who will believe the article, and repeat it. Those who question the accuracy of the story may be told, "It's true—I read it on the Internet."

Used discerningly, the Internet is a brilliant resource. These **dregs** of disinformation, however, are a hazard for the literal-minded.

---

1. What is the meaning of **oblivion**, as it is used in paragraph 1?
   a. darkness
   b. emptiness
   c. obscurity
   d. black hole

2. **Opus** comes from the Latin word opus. **Opus** most likely means
   a. story
   b. tomfoolery
   c. work
   d. falsehood

3. In paragraph 2, what does the use of the word **pallid** suggest about the speculation?
   a. It is only surface-deep.
   b. It is bogus.
   c. There is no plausibility.
   d. It is pleasing.

4. Which word means the same as **inert** as it is used in paragraph 2?
   a. motionless
   b. mysterious
   c. indelible
   d. dark

5. The word **parable** means about the same as
   a. fantasy
   b. judgment
   c. thoughtful story
   d. moral tale

6. What does **dregs** most likely mean as it is used in paragraph 4?
   a. residue
   b. misleading data
   c. lies
   d. dross

Vocabulary for Comprehension

Part 1

*Read "The Mummies of the Inca Empire," which contains words in **boldface** that appear in Units 13–15. Then answer the questions.*

The Mummies of the Inca Empire

When most people think of mummies, they probably think of the kings of ancient Egypt, whose pyramid-shaped tombs are filled with fabulous riches. But the
(5) Egyptians were not the only people who mummified their dead. The Inca Empire of Peru, which flourished long before the Spanish arrived in the Americas, left behind thousands of mummies. Archaeologists
(10) have discovered huge underground burial chambers. The mummies within these tombs and the objects buried with them are proving to be a treasure trove of clues to how the Inca lived.
(15) At its peak, the Inca Empire was the largest native state that has ever existed in the Western Hemisphere, with a population of more than 10 million. When an Inca ruler died, his body was mummified and placed
(20) within a royal tomb, along with food, drink, weapons, clothing, and mummified "helpers," including **steadfast** servants and animals. For a year after a ruler's death, his mummy was cared for as if it
(25) were still living. At the end of the year, the mummy was entombed in a great burial hall with other royal mummies, each seated on a throne. The vast wealth amassed by the kings was placed in the
(30) burial hall with them.
In Inca culture, mummies formed a link between the living and the dead. At festival times, **kindred** carried the mummies through the streets. This practice proved
(35) to people that the rulers had actually lived and that their descendants, who owned the mummies, were part of the royal line.

In the 1990s, burial chambers were discovered on a cliff high in a temperate
(40) rain forest in the Andes. Archaeologists also discovered a massive Incan graveyard in Lima, Peru. Here they unearthed the remains of more than 2000 Inca. Mummies were found wrapped in large cotton
(45) bundles that also contained food, bowls and vessels, personal items, and religious offerings. These discoveries showed that the dead in Inca society were not left to pass into **oblivion**, but rather were
(50) treasured and protected. Other mummies were found preserved in ice at the top of mountains regarded by the Inca as sacred places.
Some of these burial sites are intact.
(55) Others have been **ransacked** by thieves seeking to **plunder** gold and precious artifacts buried with the mummies. Nevertheless, each new discovery is helping scientists to increase their
(60) knowledge of these ancient people. The study of these **inert** remains is yielding details of Inca life before and after the arrival of Europeans in the Western Hemisphere. Slowly but surely,
(65) the secrets of the Inca mummies are being revealed.

1. Which statement **best** provides an inference that is supported by lines 9–14?
   A) Archeologists study plants and animals.
   B) Archaeologists design buildings and houses.
   C) Archaeologists study ancient civilizations.
   D) Archaeologists investigate contemporary burial customs.

2. As it is used in line 22, what does the word **steadfast** mean?
   A) polite
   B) faithful
   C) strong
   D) meek

3. The word **kindred** has more than one meaning. What does the word **kindred** most likely mean as it is used in line 33?
   A) relatives
   B) similar
   C) friends
   D) strangers

4. Based on the evidence in lines 34–37, why did the Inca carry mummies through the streets at festival times?
   A) to prove that they were descendants of royalty
   B) to prove that no one ever really dies
   C) to show their love for a dead relative
   D) to display the wealth of the dead person

5. What is the author's **most likely** reason for including lines 38–47?
   A) to give new information about the discovery of burial chambers
   B) to challenge archaeologists' theories about the Inca mummies
   C) to introduce an entirely new topic
   D) to describe the steps in the process of mummifying dead bodies

6. Which word means the opposite of **oblivion** in line 49?
   A) obscurity
   B) disregard
   C) esteem
   D) nothingness

7. Which phrase is closest in meaning to the word **ransacked** as it is used in line 55?
   A) left untouched
   B) visited often
   C) burned down
   D) searched thoroughly

8. As used in line 56, what does the word **plunder** mean?
   A) loot
   B) sell
   C) collect
   D) uncover

9. What does the word **inert** most likely mean as it is used in line 61?
   A) fragile
   B) ancient
   C) priceless
   D) lifeless

10. **Part A**
    Which statement about the author's point of view is **best** supported by "The Mummies of the Inca Empire"?
    A) Much can be learned about Inca civilization from its mummies.
    B) The ancient Inca Empire was weak.
    C) Spanish explorers helped create the ancient Inca civilization.
    D) The bodies of dead Inca rulers were treated like those of ordinary citizens.

    Part B
    Which sentence from the passage **best** supports your answer to Part A?
    A) "Egyptians were not the only people who mummified their dead" (lines 5–6)
    B) "after a ruler's death, his mummy was cared for" (lines 23–24)
    C) "ransacked by thieves seeking to plunder gold and precious artifacts " (lines 55–57)
    D) "each new discovery is helping scientists to increase their knowledge" (lines 58–60)

Vocabulary for Comprehension
Part 2

*Read this passage, which contains words in **boldface** that appear in Units 13–15. Then choose the best answer to each question based on what is stated or implied in the passage. You may refer to the passage as often as necessary.*

Questions 1–10 are based on the following passage.

A **forlorn** person stands outside a group, watching other people **simper** or make up witty, **wry** remarks in a social environment. While many people do
(5) not question why these actions occur, psychologists seek a **rational** explanation of human behavior. Psychology is the scientific study of the mind and its functions, especially those affecting
(10) behavior in a given context.

Although psychology is a relatively new science, with most of its newest developments occurring over the past 150 years, its roots can be traced back
(15) to ancient Greek philosophy in 400–500 BCE. During this **epoch**, Plato expressed a belief that there was a difference between body and soul. He was instrumental in establishing the idea of "mental health."
(20) He stressed that it was **crucial** to stimulate the mind with the arts. Plato influenced Aristotle, who believed that the body affected the mind. Aristotle also pleaded for scientific investigation to support
(25) any theory regarding the body and the mind—these ideas laid the foundation for modern psychology.

In the seventeenth century, René Descartes wrote that the notion of
(30) consciousness separated humans from animals. He also believed that the body influenced its consciousness. Descartes's work led to other significant philosophies of psychology by Baruch Spinoza
(35) and Gottfried Leibnitz, yet it would take another century for psychology to coalesce as a scientific discipline.

Psychology evolved as a scientific discipline in the late 1800s. In 1879,
(40) Wilhelm Wundt opened the first experimental psychology laboratory in Germany; this lab used scientific methods to study behavior. G. Stanley Hall, one of Wundt's students, founded the first
(45) U.S. experimental psychology lab at Johns Hopkins University.

Three early schools of psychology— functionalism, psychoanalysis, and structuralism—were all established in
(50) 1896. Functionalism paid careful attention to the functions of the mind rather than the thoughts of the mind. Psychoanalysis, a school founded by Sigmund Freud, stressed the importance of unconscious
(55) thoughts. Structuralism subscribed to the view that all mental experience could be understood as a combination of elements or events. Structuralism focused on what was inside the mind, thus **disclaiming**
(60) functionalism. Humanism, a later branch of psychology founded in the twentieth century, rejected traditional **strictures** in favor of an individual understanding of the world. With so many competing schools
(65) of thought, some psychologists were **haughty** about their specific approaches and scornful of others.

Today, psychology is studied in college programs across the United States.
(70) Of the 1.8 million bachelor's degrees awarded in 2011–2012, 6 percent were concentrated in psychology, making it the fourth most popular undergraduate major. Psychology will continue to be
(75) an important field as people learn how to explain what can sometimes seem inexplicable: human behavior.

1. As it is used in line 1, the word "forlorn" most nearly means
A) angry.
B) lonely.
C) healthy.
D) silly.

2. The writer includes lines 1–4 in the first paragraph to
A) provide an anecdote that readers have not encountered.
B) narrate a scenario that would confuse psychologists.
C) demonstrate an uncommon dynamic in a social environment.
D) illustrate a social interaction that would interest psychologists.

3. What is the main idea of the second paragraph?
A) Plato and Aristotle were famous Greek philosophers.
B) Plato was instrumental in establishing the idea of "mental health."
C) Psychology has its roots in ancient Greek philosophy.
D) Many developments in psychology have occurred over the past 150 years.

4. As it is used in line 16, the word "epoch" most nearly means
A) a distinct period of time.
B) a unit of measurement.
C) an important moment in history.
D) a way of viewing the world.

5. The author mentions the work of Descartes, Spinoza, and Leibnitz in order to
A) show how their specific theories influenced later psychologists.
B) contrast their theories with later psychological approaches.
C) reveal the psychological thinking of the seventeenth and early eighteenth centuries.
D) discredit their theories in light of current psychological thinking.

6. The purpose of the fourth paragraph (lines 38–46) is to
A) describe the first experimental psychology laboratory.
B) explain behaviorism as a psychological approach.
C) reveal how psychology came to be recognized as a scientific discipline.
D) compare experimental psychology labs in Germany and the United States.

7. Which approach focused not on science but on individual understanding?
A) functionalism
B) humanism
C) structuralism
D) psychoanalysis

8. Which choice provides the best evidence for the answer to the previous question?
A) Lines 50–52 ("Functionalism ... mind")
B) Lines 52–55 ("Psychoanalysis ... thoughts")
C) Lines 55–60 ("Structuralism ... functionalism")
D) Lines 60–64 ("Humanism, ... world")

9. As it is used in line 62, the word "strictures" most nearly means
A) understanding.
B) theories.
C) limitations.
D) philosophy.

10. As it is used in line 66, "haughty" most nearly means
A) supercilious.
B) ungrateful.
C) nervous.
D) confused.

Synonyms

*From the word bank below, choose the word that has the same or nearly the same meaning as the **boldface** word in each sentence and write it on the line. You will not use all of the words.*

abyss	dregs	mercenary	rational
armistice	embody	oblivion	solvent
arrogant	fiasco	opus	vendor
befall	infinite	ramshackle	waif

1. The puppy seemed to have **unlimited** energy, only slowing down when he wanted to chew on the guests' shoes. _____

2. The principal introduced the class valedictorian as a model student who never failed to **exemplify** good citizenship. _____

3. As she considered the two job offers, she knew that the **logical** decision was to take the position with higher pay instead of the lower-paying job that would allow her to follow her passion. _____

4. We wondered why the actor, whose career had seemed so promising, had faded into **obscurity**. _____

5. I would have expected such a successful person to be **overbearing**, but she was quite polite and humble. _____

6. While the public seemed to love the performer's latest song, he felt that he had yet to write his greatest **composition**. _____

7. As I moved through the busy city center, I tried to ignore each **peddler** who asked me to purchase something I didn't need. _____

8. We realized that her motivation to help us pack was purely **selfish** when we caught her stealing some valuable jewelry. _____

9. The bridge looked **rickety** from a distance, but it held up well when we began to cross it. _____

10. Your business will not remain **financially sound** if you continue to make unnecessary purchases. _____

11. Our party turned into a **disaster** when the wrong food was delivered, the rain destroyed our decorations, and several of the guests canceled. _____

12. The lottery winner decided to establish a children's home that would take in every orphan or **stray** who needed shelter. _____

Two-Word Completions

Select the pair of words that best completes the meaning of each of the following sentences.

1. "I am certainly _____ that most critics gave my play rave reviews," the author remarked. "But I can't help feeling hurt by the _____ of those who panned it."
a. estranged … enormities
b. gratified … strictures
c. vaunted … parables
d. exasperated … disclaimers

2. Acquiring a foreign language can be a(n) _____ chore because it involves so much memorization. If a person didn't have to learn everything by _____, the task would be a good deal less time-consuming.
a. tedious … rote
b. irascible … heritage
c. foreboding … epoch
d. exasperating … niche

3. Most immigrants in this country have found it necessary to _____ the traditions they brought with them from their home countries, but few have totally abandoned the rich _____ of their ancestors.
a. vilify … impediment
b. amplify … kindred
c. adapt … heritage
d. plunder … veneer

4. "Critics claim that my support for human rights has never been anything but halfhearted," the senator remarked. "However, the record shows that I have been _____ in my commitment to this great cause. Indeed, I take great pride in the fact that I have never _____ in my allegiance to it."
a. inert … adapted
b. bland … malingered
c. negligent … loitered
d. steadfast … faltered

5. "You don't need to address issues that will clearly have no effect on the outcome of this election," the campaign manager told the candidate. "But it is _____ for you to take a firm stand on those issues that may ultimately prove _____."
a. imperative … crucial
b. gratifying … pallid
c. naive … reciprocal
d. tedious … bland

6. I love to host dinner parties, but I seldom serve _____ food. I like to spice things up. My signature appetizer, Furious Fava Bean Dip, will not completely _____ your taste buds, but it will make your tongue tingle!
a. pallid … garnish
b. bland … obliterate
c. pithy … plunder
d. irascible … ransack

7. Though police officers in my neighborhood are sometimes accused of _____, let me point out that the diligence with which they solve most cases clearly _____ their overall devotion to duty.
a. negligence … disclaims
b. steadfastness … dovetails with
c. malingering … attests to
d. inertia … obliterates

WORD STUDY

Idioms

In the passage "Working Like a Dog" (see pages 156–157), the trainer tells the interviewer that he enjoys watching the dogs "chow down" after a long day of training. "Chow down" is an idiom that means "to eat something quickly and hungrily."

Idioms are words, phrases, or sayings whose meanings are figurative, not literal. When you hear a new idiom, think about the context in which it is used. Consider how the literal meaning might point to a more abstract meaning. Listen also to the speaker's tone: Is the idiom playful, critical, or matter-of-fact?

Choosing the Right Idiom

Read each sentence. Use context clues to figure out the meaning of each idiom in **boldface** *print. Then write the letter of the definition for the idiom in the sentence.*

1. Andrew thinks a successful salesperson has to **come on strong** to customers, but I disagree. _____

2. My brother has Friday off, but I'll be heading **back to the salt mines.** _____

3. Getting a window office was the **icing on the cake** after I got my promotion and pay raise. _____

4. Todd **got off on the wrong foot** with his supervisor, but later he impressed her with a great idea. _____

5. It doesn't matter whether the traffic accident was caused by speeding or by carelessness; **it amounts to the same thing.** _____

6. Don't tease Jasmine about falling off the horse yesterday; you'll just **rub salt in the wound.** _____

7. Kim buys cookies at the corner bakery because they always pack **a baker's dozen.** _____

8. Miguel was **on pins and needles** waiting for the result of his math exam. _____

9. Although the defendant was guilty, all he got was **a slap on the wrist.** _____

10. Grace **made no bones about** her decision to vote for Judge Lowden. _____

a. thirteen

b. anxious or nervous

c. was clear and direct about

d. an extra benefit on top of something that's already good

e. back to work

f. act aggressively and forcefully

g. a mild punishment

h. the outcome is the same either way

i. started off poorly

j. make something painful even worse

Classical Roots

fect, fic, efy, ify—to make

This Latin root appears in **amplify** (page 206), which means "to make bigger, increase." Some other words based on the same root are listed below.

beneficial	clarify	deify	exemplify
certify	defective	edify	personify

From the list of words above, choose the one that corresponds to each of the brief definitions below. Write the word in the blank space in the illustrative sentence below the definition. Use a dictionary if necessary.

1. favorable, helpful, producing good (*"making good"*)

The _____ influence of teachers has helped many young people to realize their full potential.

2. to make a god of; to worship as a god

The ancient Romans _____ the emperors Julius Caesar and Augustus posthumously.

3. faulty, not perfect, not complete

Manufacturers will often replace _____ products free of charge.

4. to guarantee; to declare true or correct (*"make certain"*)

A notary public _____ that documents, such as deeds and contracts, are authentic.

5. to be an example of; to show by example

Awards were presented to students whose conduct _____ the principles of good citizenship and service to the community.

6. to make clear or easier to understand

A flowchart can be used to _____ the steps in any operation.

7. to be the embodiment of; to represent the qualities of

In an old-fashioned melodrama, the hero _____ courage and virtue.

8. to instruct so as to encourage intellectual, moral, or spiritual improvement

A sermon should _____ those who hear it.

Synonyms

Select the two words or expressions that are most nearly the same in meaning.

1. **a.** ostracize   **b.** exasperate   **c.** waver   **d.** vex
2. **a.** abashed   **b.** pertinent   **c.** rational   **d.** relevant
3. **a.** willful   **b.** exotic   **c.** wanton   **d.** aghast
4. **a.** prone   **b.** aloof   **c.** predatory   **d.** apt
5. **a.** stricture   **b.** ruse   **c.** foreboding   **d.** premonition
6. **a.** plunder   **b.** ravage   **c.** bolster   **d.** grope
7. **a.** annul   **b.** obsess   **c.** invalidate   **d.** assert
8. **a.** personable   **b.** arrogant   **c.** overbearing   **d.** facetious
9. **a.** appease   **b.** mediate   **c.** belittle   **d.** minimize
10. **a.** proclaim   **b.** tether   **c.** negate   **d.** nullify
11. **a.** bountiful   **b.** ample   **c.** congested   **d.** capacious
12. **a.** pithy   **b.** resolute   **c.** steadfast   **d.** curt
13. **a.** muster   **b.** amass   **c.** hover   **d.** excise
14. **a.** crucial   **b.** vaunted   **c.** inaudible   **d.** pivotal
15. **a.** convey   **b.** waver   **c.** falter   **d.** wallow

Antonyms

Select the two words or expressions that are most nearly opposite in meaning.

16. **a.** kindred   **b.** blasé   **c.** dexterous   **d.** fervent
17. **a.** cryptic   **b.** jaunty   **c.** forlorn   **d.** gaunt
18. **a.** inert   **b.** volatile   **c.** menial   **d.** oblique
19. **a.** incapacitate   **b.** articulate   **c.** scoff   **d.** rehabilitate
20. **a.** vigil   **b.** antics   **c.** elite   **d.** dregs
21. **a.** entail   **b.** comply   **c.** preclude   **d.** loiter
22. **a.** disdain   **b.** wrangle   **c.** venerate   **d.** sustain
23. **a.** renown   **b.** oblivion   **c.** unison   **d.** niche
24. **a.** proximity   **b.** promontory   **c.** abyss   **d.** juncture
25. **a.** retentive   **b.** porous   **c.** belated   **d.** servile

Two-Word Completions

Select the pair of words that best completes the meaning of each of the following sentences.

26. The spectators at the lion cage were amused to see the seemingly _____ animal eat in such a(n) _____ manner.

a. voracious … gingerly   **c.** irascible … whimsical

b. disarming … tedious   **d.** unassuming … unflagging

27. As a child _____, Mozart basked in public praise and attention from an early age, _____ his talents all around Europe.

a. laggard … tainting   **c.** turncoat … obliterating

b. prodigy … flaunting   **d.** mendicant … ruing

28. Though his father had _____ frugal spending habits in him, the young man misspent his first paycheck on _____ purchases.

a. ferreted … solvent   **c.** bestowed … bland

b. instilled … frivolous   **d.** attested … caustic

29. The young couple could see that the _____ house, while charming, was in _____ need of repair.

a. plebeian … perceptible   **c.** ramshackle … dire

b. ungainly … prodigious   **d.** indiscriminate … plausible

30. I admired her ability to keep a completely calm _____ and _____ manner even in the most stressful situations.

a. doctrine… infinite   **c.** embargo … haggard

b. recipient … naive   **d.** mien … judicious

31. I felt like a complete _____ after a day of fruitless job searching, but my dog still thinks I am a _____ king.

a. nonentity… veritable   **c.** citadel… incognito

b. fiasco … skittish   **d.** addendum… forthright

32. The stranger's ominous remark struck a _____ note in the playful _____ at the garden party.

a. avowed … juncture   **c.** discordant … banter

b. pert … perspective   **d.** personable … veneer

Supplying Words in Context

To complete each sentence, select the best word from among the choices given. Not all words in the word bank will be used. You may modify the word form as necessary.

abut	endow	fend	plaudits
avail	ensue	malinger	purge
deplore	estrange	ornate	ransack
disgruntled	ethical	pallid	shiftless
embody	evolve	peruse	vie

33. A riot may _____ if the crowd is not properly controlled.

34. The fans were _____ because they were convinced that their team had lost as the result of bad officiating.

35. We had to _____ every room in the house in order to find the missing book.

36. How can the employers expect any one applicant for the job to _____ *all* the qualities they are seeking?

37. Before you fill out the job application, you should _____ the instructions carefully.

38. Unless he improves his _____ ways, he will not be successful at that job.

adage	finesse	myriad	staid
audacious	glut	opus	stoical
decoy	impediment	parry	trepidation
devoid	impending	scavenger	vilify
fallacy	levity	simper	waif

39. The defense attorney prematurely remarked that the lack of solid evidence against her client would make the _____ trial an effortless victory.

40. The _____ professor refused to keep up with the advancements in his field, and felt that his students' avant-garde papers were outlandish.

41. With my friend serving as a(n) _____ to attract their attention, we managed to get away without their seeing us.

42. Of all the _____ woes of humankind, is there anything worse than a toothache?

43. In preparation for the big meet, the track team had a big dinner the night before, feasting on a(n) _____ of pasta and bread.

44. *Adventures of Huckleberry Finn* is doubtless Mark Twain's most famous and most controversial _____.

Word Associations

*Select the word or expression that best completes the meaning of the sentence or answers the question, with particular reference to the meaning of the word in **boldface** type.*

45. People who have reached an **accord**
  a. are in agreement
  b. work at similar jobs
  c. play musical instruments
  d. are at the last stop of a bus line

46. To do something without **stinting** is to be
  a. in bad taste
  b. generous
  c. stingy
  d. careful

47. **Apparitions** would be likely to play an important part in
  a. a TV news program
  b. a math examination
  c. ghost stories
  d. your history book

48. A **pseudonym** is most likely to be used by
  a. a waif
  b. someone traveling incognito
  c. a leading citizen of your community
  d. a police officer

49. A **recluse** usually prefers to be
  a. in good company
  b. out-of-doors
  c. alone
  d. in a position of power

50. Which of the following might aptly be classified as **wry**?
  a. twinge of conscience
  b. a mole
  c. a loaf of bread
  d. a sense of humor

51. The **jurisdiction** of a court refers to
  a. the money needed to run the court
  b. the qualifications of the judges
  c. where the court is located
  d. the kinds of cases it can decide

52. Which of the following might be called **tawdry**?
  a. a one-room schoolhouse
  b. cheap, loud decorations
  c. a well-managed farm
  d. a center for medical research

53. A person who serves as your **proxy** is
  a. one who acts in your place
  b. a close friend
  c. a servant
  d. a medical specialist

54. A **parable** uses a story to
  a. make arithmetical computations
  b. trap a liar
  c. clarify a moral idea
  d. describe an event

55. The word **teeming** would not be applied to
  a. an empty room
  b. a jungle
  c. the streets of a busy city
  d. a heavy rainfall

56. A **tractable** person is one who
  a. is unbearably stubborn
  b. is easily influenced by others
  c. can operate a tractor
  d. owns a large tract of land

Choosing the Right Meaning

Read each sentence carefully. Then select the item that best completes the statement below the sentence.

57. On the first day of school, the teacher told his students that doing their homework was **imperative** for achieving academic success.

    The word **imperative** most nearly means

    a. expensive   **b.** terrifying   **c.** burdensome   **d.** essential

58. Firefighters spent four days putting out the **calamitous** fire that burned down half the city.

    The word **calamitous** most nearly means

    a. brief   **b.** devastating   **c.** minor   **d.** sudden

59. Even though his manner of speaking is full of **quirks**, he is a great lecturer.

    The word **quirks** most nearly means

    a. ideas   **b.** mistakes   **c.** failures   **d.** peculiarities

60. The world-renowned opera singer **basked** in the limelight.

    The word **basked** most nearly means

    a. flourished   **b.** faded   **c.** reveled   **d.** hid

61. After much experimentation, the scientists finally **devised** a method for eliminating hiccups in mice.

    The word **devised** most nearly means

    a. borrowed   **b.** discarded   **c.** explained   **d.** invented

62. They had such **divergent** points of view that the two coworkers could not agree on how to execute the project.

    The word **divergent** most nearly means

    a. differing   **b.** similar   **c.** interesting   **d.** conventional

63. The animal welfare officers inspecting the neglected zoo were dismayed by how the animals **cowered** in their cages.

    The word **cowered** most nearly means

    a. slept   **b.** cringed   **c.** roared   **d.** growled

64. Her travel plans went **awry** when all the bus drivers suddenly went on strike.

    The word **awry** most nearly means

    a. slowly   **b.** forward   **c.** smoothly   **d.** amiss

65. It's astonishing how many adults still believe in the **legendary** Loch Ness Monster.

    The word **legendary** most nearly means

    a. historical   **b.** foreign   **c.** mythical   **d.** fascinating

The following is a list of all the words taught in the Units of this book. The number after each entry indicates the page on which the word is defined.

abashed, 82
abdicate, 170
abut, 114
abyss, 214
accord, 146
acme, 106
adage, 18
adapt, 194
addendum, 70
aghast, 70
allot, 38
aloof, 86
amass, 42
ample, 74
amplify, 206
anguish, 86
annul, 62
antics, 30
apparition, 74
appease, 162
apt, 130
armistice, 202
arrogant, 206
articulate, 82
assert, 74
attest, 190
attire, 114
attribute, 102
audacious, 38
avail, 118
avowed, 26
awry, 126

banter, 30
barter, 150
bask, 86
befall, 218
belated, 158
belittle, 106
bestow, 174

bland, 202
blasé, 62
bludgeon, 126
bolster, 58
bonanza, 14
bountiful, 26

calamitous, 162
capacious, 170
capitulate, 130
caustic, 174
chafe, 126
churlish, 14
citadel, 18
cite, 158
collaborate, 14
comply, 38
congested, 26
conventional, 158
convey, 102
cower, 70
crony, 114
crucial, 214
crusade, 170
cryptic, 118
curt, 146

decoy, 158
decree, 18
deface, 170
defect, 82
defile, 130
delve, 162
deplore, 58
detriment, 30
devise, 150
devoid, 42
dexterous, 150
dire, 126
disarming, 130

disclaim, 202
discordant, 18
disdain, 74
disgruntled, 130
divergent, 114
doctrine, 106
dovetail, 190
dregs, 218
durable, 30

elite, 42
embargo, 174
embody, 214
encroach, 126
endow, 130
engross, 146
enmity, 118
enormity, 194
ensue, 158
entail, 146
enterprising, 26
epitaph, 70
epoch, 206
estrange, 206
ethical, 70
evolve, 18
exasperate, 218
excerpt, 14
excise, 106
exotic, 102

facetious, 74
fallacy, 170
falter, 194
fend, 126
ferret, 150
fervent, 118
fiasco, 214
finesse, 86
flaunt, 82

foreboding, 194
forlorn, 190
forthright, 86
frivolous, 58
frugal, 30

gallantry, 162
garnish, 214
gaunt, 114
genial, 82
gingerly, 26
glut, 26
grapple, 38
gratify, 202
grope, 14

habituate, 150
haggard, 102
haughty, 194
heritage, 218
hover, 18

impart, 162
impediment, 194
impending, 146
imperative, 190
impunity, 130
inaudible, 70
incapacitate, 42
incognito, 26
indiscriminate, 74
inert, 218
infiltrate, 118
infinite, 202
instigate, 38
instill, 86
intrigue, 70
invalidate, 30
irascible, 206

WORD LIST